Peter Noever (ed.)

**VISIONARY CLIENTS
FOR NEW ARCHITECTURE**

VISIONARY CLIENTS
FOR NEW ARCHITECTURE

Edited by Peter Noever / MAK

With an Essay by Joseph Rykwert and Comments by Philip Johnson

Prestel

Munich · London · New York

This book is published on the occasion of the MAK lecture series YOU DA MAN! –
Visionary Clients for New Architecture, which took place in November and December 1998 at the MAK
– Austrian Museum of Applied Arts, Stubenring 5, A-1010 Vienna, Austria, Tel. (+43-1) 711 36-0,
Fax (+43-1) 713 10 26, e-mail: office@mak.at

Cover: Zaha Hadid, Vitra Fire Station (photo courtesy of Vitra, Photograph by Richard Bryant)

Library of Congress Card Number: 99-069838

Die Deutsche Bibliothek – CIP-Einheitsaufnahme
Visionary clients for new Architecture / ed.: Peter Noever. – München : Prestel, 2000
    ISBN 3-7913-2296-6

Prestel Verlag
Mandlstrasse 26, D-80802 Munich, Germany
Tel. +49 (89) 38 17 09-0, Fax +49 (89) 38 17 09-35
4 Bloomsbury Place, London WC1A 2QA
Tel. +44 (0171) 323-5004, Fax +44 (0171) 636-8004
and 175 Fifth Avenue, Suite 402, New York, NY 10010, USA
Tel. (646) 602-8616, Fax (646) 602-8639

Prestel books are available worldwide. Please contact your nearest bookseller
or write to any of the above addresses for information concerning your local distributor.

Percept: Peter Noever
General editor: Bettina M. Busse
Assistant: Cornelia Greber
Copy editing: Claudia Mazanek, Peter Meredith
Translations: Maria E. Clay, Kimi Lum
Graphic design: Büro Perndl, Vienna
Design: Verlagsservice G. Pfeifer, Germering
Typesetting: EDV-Fotosatz Huber, Germering
Lithography: Repro Line, Munich
Printing and binding: Druckerei Huber, Dießen

Printed in Germany on acid-free paper

ISBN 3-7913-2296-6

CONTENTS

YOU DA MAN!
YOU ARE THE MAN!
YOU ARE MY MAN!
THE PLANNING CAN BEGIN.

Peter Noever

Relief and enthusiasm appear on both sides when a client has found an architect who does not squelch all his fantasies and visions with doubts, problems of material constraints and feasibility studies. On the other hand, the architect is relieved to find a client who does not pettily weigh cost and benefit, insisting on efficiency, but instead demands an unconditional architecture which realizes its heady, ebullient, striking artistic qualities. Even if the first encounter between client and architect occurs with such intensity, the end result of their collaboration might not be an actual building. Again and again such symbiotic alliances – like love affairs – end in mutual curses, lawsuits and often countersuits. In successful cases, however, this symbiosis will result in exceptional architecture, true "Baukunst" – the art of building – which does not hide its passionate qualities and in turn provokes public passion, idolizing veneration alternating with wild invectives.

Complaints about overly luxurious buildings have been voiced since antiquity. In the 12th century St. Bernard of Clairvaux, a client who commissioned an abbey, stated that it was not right to cover stone walls with gold while the poor had to go naked. In a modified form this argument still has a considerable following. It tacitly postulates that architecture, as an intervention in public space, has to meet with public approval. Such arguments miss the crux of the matter. To be sure, no architecture, however magnificent, will ease the fate of the poor. It is doubtful that the poor would be helped if buildings were more austere and cheaper: social problems can rarely be solved by a mere redistribution of money.

The results of architectural competitions show the devastating consequences that occur when public consensus is the guiding principle affecting decisions for urban planning. The outcome is an extremely boring mainstream architecture, determined by a jury's search for harmony as it attempts to mediate between diverse interest groups: the clients who measure their ideas of representation and usability merely by economic considerations; the urban planners who all too often fear innovations as destructive interventions in the familiar urban identity; and the neighbours who regard any new building in the vicinity with scepticism because it will involve a lot of noise. For this reason even the competition will usually play it safe, with details that represent a distilled version of the concerns of various interest groups. Additionally, new and ever more elaborate building codes and regulations need to be observed. The designs of most major urban planning projects are interchangeable and rarely go beyond the mediocre. Recent examples of such mediocrity are found in the competitions for the various new building projects in the center of Berlin.

There are certainly other possible points of departure. If clients can free themselves from the prevailing standards and find a congenial architect for their projects, the first and decisive hurdle has been taken towards leaving the beaten track and developing a new architectural language. This is best represented by Renaissance architecture, in which the political climate in the city-states of northern Italy provided the prerequisites for such seemingly modern partnerships: "Liberation of ideas, disregard for authorities, the victory of education over the conceit of descent, an enthusiasm for science and the scientific past of man, unfettering the individual, an ardent love of truth,"[1] as Nietzsche has described it. The break with the old feudal system and the reorganization of the economic and social structures created the necessary preconditions for a new and advanced architecture. A critical mass of technological, economic and cultural resources was now available to a social class which had not come to it by descent or divine right and which did not display arrogance towards the lower classes. In addition to the dependent court architects who linked their fate to that of their princely patrons for better or for worse, a new class of independent architects arose who developed their own individuality first and then searched and found their clients. Thus, both architects and clients belonged to the same social class. It was against this background that the rich bourgeois families like the Sforzas in Milan and the Medici in Florence encountered a well-educated group of architects trained in antiquity and humanist philosophy. The basis of this process was both an idea shared by client and architect and the courage to take risks on both sides. The dependent court architects were replaced by independent master architects who obtained their commissions on the basis of their personal concept of architecture.

This scenario has changed little to this day. Architects are by definition independent and operate in a free market, but country-specific restrictions such as building codes or socially motivated, standardized ideas are still quite common and influential. It is up to the individuals concerned to determine how these remaining possibilities are used. In other words, the circumstances are not so adverse to good architecture. Yet we wonder why there are so few outstanding building projects. Both sides do not always have sufficient potential for experimentation and risk-taking. Particularly in the field of public commissions, bureaucratic decision-making hierarchies are an obstacle not only in terms of design approval but also with regard to decisions to build. The few officials committed to good architecture cannot really prevent the unimpressive conglomeration of mediocre buildings catering to the lowest com-

---

1 Friedrich Nietzsche, *Menschliches – Allzumenschliches* (Leipzig 1889), p. 65 [*Human – All-too-Human*, 1909–11].

mon denominator in many cities. The ignorance of the chosen representatives of the people and officials in charge goes hand in hand with the modest expectations of their clients. The situation is similar in major projects by multinational companies where early in the planning stages care is taken that the corporate identity is preserved exactly in the version in which it has been defined. The resulting "shoeboxes" of steel, glass and marble claim originality, yet they differ as little from one another as the hamburgers of different fast-food chains. Whether or not the architect is a star, his/her influence is kept to a minimum. Innovative architecture is risky and unpredictable: investors do not appreciate incalculable risks. Moreover, the relationship between client and architect is subject to other pitfalls as well. It is dangerous if the client simply wants the architect to design a building within a specific framework of time and money and does not really get involved in the planning himself/herself. Conversely, if the client regards the architect as a mere agent of his building fantasies and if the architect's irrepressible desire to build submits to the client's whims and self-aggrandizements, the result will be an eclectic, lay architecture. "It is at this critical point that we individually make our deal with the devil and then live with the consequences. The devil in each project comes with many faces; sometimes it is pure economic greed, sometimes it's self-aggrandizement, sometimes it's political manipulation …"[2] Frank Gehry writes about these dangers, the greatest of which has been and still is in architects working for the powers that be. Political rulers interested in manifesting their power in the architecture of their cities have almost limitless power over resources and money and may seduce architects into trading their convictions for a life of luxury and the lure of power: "The architects favored by Stalin saw themselves as the elite. They demanded exorbitant fees, lived in luxurious apartments, worked in expensively outfitted studios (…). Whatever disadvantages this situation might entail, it entitled them to hope to be able to realize even their most eccentric ideas, as long as they enjoyed the support of the most powerful instance in the country (…). Tyrants have always had a weakness for architects and builders."[3]

On the other hand – though in an entirely different manner – our democratic society, which is often devoted exclusively to economic considerations, has developed a standard that permits "less and less architecture." This is reflected in counterproductive regulations and a general standardization of building elements, which may be explained by fashion as well as standardized wishes and desires.

While dictators are concerned with the representation of their power to impress the masses, many companies are interested in the demonstration of prestige that is likewise meant to impress the masses and in this way serve as effective advertising. For this reason, more and more architects are being hired to design interesting images for their clients, with the interiors turned over to "space planners," interior designers, and various kinds of engineers. When Johnson was hired to design the new headquarters for AT&T, in Manhattan, his client (the telephone company) was primarily concerned with creating a striking image for its headquar-

---

2 Frank O. Gehry, "Preface," in: Peter Noever (ed.), *The End of Architecture?* (Munich 1993), p. 11.
3 Alexej Tarchanow/Sergej Kawtaradse, *Stalinistische Architektur* (Munich 1992), p. 10.

ters, and in fact the client retained other experts to do the office interiors, the structural frame, the environmental equipment and one or two other things inside the skin of the finished "image" which was the real concern of the marketing experts who hired the architects.[4] The fact that Johnson was able to assert himself with an individualistic architecture is less due to the intense cooperation between architect and client than to the fact that the decision makers at AT&T gave him more latitude than usual. However, even in this situation, the architect had to observe the conditions from which he was exempt when he combined the functions of both client and architect in one person and therefore assumed the overall responsibility for the design and its realization.

The achievement of architecture is best demonstrated by Johnson in the Glass House, built for himself in New Canaan, Connecticut, in 1949. Johnson's longing for "pure architecture" is represented in this house by an uncompromising manifestation of certain inalienable ideas. This approach to architecture as empirical fundamental artistic research is also found in the work of other architects who have acted as clients themselves. The Mexican, Luis Barragán, an outspoken critic of the faceless international building style of glass and steel, experimented in his residential buildings with influences of regional architecture and urged his colleagues to see the designing of buildings as a dialogue with the landscape. Günther Domenig's own house, the *Steinhaus* [Stone House] in Steindorf in Carinthia, may be called a landscape of concrete for us to live in with a life of its own, a belligerent, attacking structure, a personal sign of an individualistic nonconformist: "In every sense I have reached the limit; this will show what I am capable of achieving in architecture. I have reached the limit of my own self. I am faced with the limit of the technical possibilities as well as my financial possibilities: there is no way out, no way back. I feel the futility of my own consistency, the better I am, the better every single step becomes, the more difficult the next one will become, and perhaps I will fail in it."[5] As a curator of his own huge "museum district," Donald Judd, the great artist and most outspoken critic of architecture, was able to explore in Marfa, Texas, as though in a laboratory, the way in which his art finds its equivalent in architecture. Likewise as his own client, Frank O. Gehry built his own residence in Santa Monica in 1971–77. However, the union of client and architect in one person, a symbiosis that functions and works very well, must by no means be regarded as a generally valid model of architecture.

Good architecture has rarely been created without friction between the individuals and the content involved. If both architect and client have strong personalities, their agreement about fundamental architectural questions may be of lesser importance than their mutual attraction. When Herbert F. Johnson, the grandson of the founder of the Johnson Wax Company in Illinois, rejected existing plans for a conservative office building and turned to Frank Lloyd Wright instead, it was a memorable encounter which the client later summed up laconically: "He had a Lincoln Zephyr, and I had one – that was the only thing we agreed on. On

4   Peter Blake, "Philip Johnson – Biography," in: Peter Noever (ed.), *Philip Johnson: Turning Point* (Vienna 1997), p. 49.
5   "Das Haus des Architekten," in: MAK (ed.), *Günther Domenig: Das Steinhaus* (Vienna 1988), p. 13.

all other matters we were at each other's throats."[6] Nevertheless Wright was commissioned to design the building, but the relationship of the two partners during the building process was subject to numerous constraints that lead to personal strain. Complex room schedules, new and experimental building and planning methods on the one hand and a tight schedule and limited budget on the other hand result in a kind of natural opposition. Further, there are differences in taste and imagination. The number of quarrels is legion, and many a lawyer still lives quite well on controversies that were eventually settled in the courts.

The present publication presents clients whose attempts to realize their ideas in collaboration with an architect did not lead to a court case. The starting point for this book was a series of talks organized in the fall of 1998 by the Museum of Applied Arts in Vienna on the topic of "Visionary Clients and New Architecture." The talks were not given by the architects, but by the clients whose involvement has made an essential contribution to new approaches and positions in architecture. From the few "ideal" clients who exist, Frederick Samitaur Smith, Thomas Krens and Rolf Fehlbaum were selected to come to Vienna and talk about their projects. Smith discussed his collaboration with Eric Owen Moss on their joint project, Culver City in Los Angeles County, which is still far from completed; Thomas Krens, the innovative director of the Guggenheim Foundation, spoke about the development of Frank O. Gehry's Guggenheim Museum in Bilbao; and Rolf Fehlbaum talked about his life's work, the Vitra factory complex, which like Culver City is unfinished. The Vitra factory complex in Weil am Rhein, where such diverse architects as Nicholas Grimshaw, Tadao Ando, Frank O. Gehry, Zaha Hadid and Alvaro Siza have been commissioned to build extraordinary buildings, doubles as a kind of architectural museum of the avant-garde.

Considering that standardized construction methods that dominate the world over are based on misunderstood economic considerations in an economically functioning system, these examples of successful collaborations between client and planning architect provide an alternative to the usual way of commissioning a building. A successful relationship between architect and (private) client is not necessarily based on an inexhaustible financial background; rather it is based on a lively and alert interest in architects, whether they are internationally known or emerging. In addition, successful projects are distinguished by the fact that they are able to combine a visionary formulation with a realistic assessment of what is feasible and what can be financed. Rolf Fehlbaum's project of the Vitra factory complex is paradigmatic for this approach, though he took it one step further. He confronts the architects and architecture with ever new challenges by placing them in a communicative context: no matter which architect is invited to design a new building, the design has to respond to the existing buildings and hence to his colleagues' architecture. In this way architecture becomes an experiment for everyone involved, the client, the architect and last but not least for anyone interested in architecture.

---

6 Quoted from: Brian Carter, *Johnson Wax Administration Building and Research Tower* (London 1988), p. 5.

Once again, in regards to Bilbao, it becomes clear in Thomas Krens' description that the municipal politicians of this Basque city were courageous enough to offer an extraordinary building site and to believe that an international art museum could provide a strong impulse – even economically – for the city and the entire region. They were not disappointed: the building changed the whole appearance of the city and gave it an attractiveness that radiates way beyond the borders of the country. In the near future new and diverse impulses may likewise be expected from the building planned for the Guggenheim Museum by Thomas Krens and Frank O. Gehry on the Hudson Pier in New York City. In any case the result of the symbiosis of an extraordinary site with an apparently proven team will be promising and exciting. It is also certain that what will ensure a steady stream of interested visitors will not only be the possibility of seeing the holdings of the museum that have so far been hidden in the reserves but also the building itself. These projects are exemplary of the status of architecture: it is much more than the mere furnishing of the urban landscape; it justifiedly meets the same respect as the classical works of the visual arts. The fad that we may see a new form of cultural tourism here must not tempt us into adapting the art itself – whether architecture or the visual arts – to this new taste of the masses.

The primary essence of architecture constitutes itself in the field of tension between theory and practice, universal claim and archaic character, but in order to create spaces that are indebted to their period of origin as well as beyond, its continuous processive character must also be assured without any qualifications. Any society that builds, commissions architects that conform to its ideas. In this way architecture is definitely a reflection of a society's political and cultural self-image.

Critical questions about architecture and its historical context are the beginning and precondition of any well-founded theoretical reflection about architecture: Can a radical and unmistakable position on architecture be taken up by this uncompromising involvement of the clients and architects mentioned? And can the buildings for art that result from jointly realized visions do justice to the guiding principles of today's art production?

The architectural program of even the most renowned architect does not guarantee success, unless a congenial client can be found with precise ideas and concrete demands of the joint work. This constant interaction of client and architect is the true essence of authoritative projects – especially if they have an entirely successful aura like the buildings presented here. When all is said and done the question thus remains: how we can make sure that the new qualities of progressive architecture will not lose their chance for long-term effects; that these qualities will in fact be influential and will not be watered down into a mere fashionable attitude in subsequent buildings? These questions remain unanswered, but they come up again and again with every new collaboration, every new project, every new building.

SECOND THOUGHTS

Joseph Rykwert

Museum directors used not to care for architecture. Some twenty years ago one – and a very distinguished one – confessed to me that the museum he would like to run should be a series of interconnected boxes, white on the inside and with no exterior to speak of. With that in mind, Hans Hollein, the only true ironist among recent architects, designed his "ideal-experimental" museum as an elevated tunnel that had a mechanical "easel" opposite the entrance on which the spectator, elevated above earthly cares, could contemplate one painting at a time, which would be fetched up from the reserves by a hydraulic jack. That was some forty years ago, just before the great museum inflation.

In spite of my friend's wish, museums have – since the eighteenth century – been treated as public institutions. The great collections which princes and potentates turned over to the public required a dignified setting, worthy of the donor. The Vatican, the Louvre, the Residences in Dresden and Munich, gradually acquired museum-gallery adjuncts, some of which were the work of distinguished architects – but they were adjuncts nonetheless. The Glyptothek and the Pinakothek in Munich, though, were different – they were civic buildings, not palace adjuncts, part of an ambitious new urban layout, though not as ambitious as the New (now Old) Museum which the King (Frederick William IV) had built by Schinkel in Berlin at about the same time. Schinkel operated the elements of the building in a cunning way: the long frontal colonnade, the exterior stairways, the enfilades of galleries became the model of how a national museum should look. With the old palace, the grand arsenal building and the new Cathedral, it was to create a forum for the city. Within a decade the old royal stables in London had been razed and the National Gallery was built on the site, framing a new civic space, Trafalgar Square. In Vienna a quarter of a century later the huge Natural History and Art-Historical Museums were designed to face each other across the Ringstraße from the imperial palace, the Hofburg, in a vast Kaiserforum. Their principal architect, Gottfried Semper, had earlier built the Dresden museum (after the collection was moved out of the royal palace) and Opera house as part of a civic project as ambitious as any of the others. On the other hand, the Metropolitan Museum in New York was not planted in Central Park – against the opposition of its landscape architect, Frederick Law Olmsted – until 1880.

The great civic museums built in emulation of these royal examples were very much nineteenth-century institutions. They were monumental – sometimes overpowering – palatial and paternalistic, since they were intended to bring the blessings of an elevated elite taste to the people and to create an enlightened public among the middle and (hopefully also) the lower classes. Of course, like many institutions, they were ruled by conservative curators and historians. Artists were admitted onto their walls after a preliminary vetting and a selection through various salons. And that is why, once the avant-garde became the dominant force in the creative world, they were seen as bastions to be attacked. Marinetti's war-cries demanding the burning of museums and the destruction of monuments are so well known that they hardly need to be repeated in full: "Let them come, the jolly incendiaries with their charred fingers! Here they are! Here they are! ... Get on! Set fire to the library shelves! ... Divert canals to flood the museums! Oh the joy of seeing the famous old canvases drifting away, all shredded and discoloured."[1]

He goes on and on. These exhortations no longer seem quite so cheerful and "futuristic"– we have passed through too many book-burnings since then.

At the time, however, they had a limited but powerful appeal. Of course, not all artists, however "advanced," held such views. Many of them continued to look at and copy old masters in the museums. Moreover, the Cubists and the Expressionists discovered anthropological-ethnographic collections as an alternative source of formal invention. What is clear is that all these artists also wanted to see the works of their rebellious predecessors rather than the displays of official patronage – and this forced a change in the policy and the status of the galleries of modern art. In the second half of the nineteenth century, museums intended to house contemporary paintings began to appear in capital cities, but lack of clear direction on the part of the patronage, major wars and financial crises in the early twentieth century proved to be something of a damper and caused a hiatus in their development. Having been caught napping, they then became sometimes too eager to appear up-to-date. In any case, they were soon confronted with the problem stated sharply in the mythic-heroic postcard Gertrude Stein sent to Alfred Barr (who was fishing for the bequest of her Picasso portrait): "either you're a museum or you're modern." And in the end, she bequeathed the picture to the Metropolitan Museum, not to the Museum of Modern Art.

Such asperity was all very well at a time when collectors bought pictures for their own delight – and of course they still do that. But from about 1960 on many pictures were steadily getting larger. Pollock's method of painting required larger canvases than those of most of his contemporaries, and it soon became obvious that museums were changing not just in size, but in scale: the Museum of Modern Art, then, after the war, the Guggenheim and the Whitney in New York, were followed by others in Los Angeles, Chicago, Boston, and San Francisco – all of them with more wall surface than their current collections could reputably cover.

---

1 "E vengano dunque, gli allegri incendiarii dalle dita carbonizzate! Eccoli! Eccoli! ... Suvvia! Date fuoco agli scaffali delle biblioteche! ... Sviate il corso dei canali, per inondare i musei! ... Oh, la gioia di veder galleggiare alla deriva, lacere e stinte su quelle acque, le vecchie tele gloriose..." F. T. Marinetti, *Fondazione e Manifesto del Futurismo*.

An American composer once pointed out to me that as long as the 78 rpm wax records were current, musicians were turning out five to seven minute pieces; with the arrival of the high-fidelity vinyl disks they tended to prefer a 25-minute format. And of course, now that we have magnetic tape and the CD, they can opt for hour-long pieces. There is nothing cynical about this – any more than there is about writing sonnets. It is both natural and right for artists to accept and to play with physical constraints. In the particular case of the relation between artists and museums, there was certainly an interplay – perhaps the canvases and the sculptures got bigger even before there was room for them on museum walls. However, this rise in the scale of the works and the galleries which sheltered them had the consequence of making the buildings as imposing – in bulk, if not in aspect – as the civic institutions of the mid-nineteenth century. As the public flocked to them in a new way, so artists ventured beyond their accepted roles, and the very nature of their craft changed. Kurt Schwitters' *Merzbau*, begun in Hannover in 1920, was re-made in Norway and later (1944) as the *Merzbarn* at Elterwater in the Lake District (always in his private quarters) was partly financed by the Museum of Modern Art in New York. It defied conservation, and – unfinished – it was moved to a university museum in Newcastle-upon-Tyne. With the advent of performance art, body art – and even more, earth art – the relationship between artists and museums became increasingly problematic.

The museum therefore found itself in an undefined and unprecedented situation. It was clearly not prepared for the huge influx of visitors in the '60s and '70s which started with the mega-exhibitions. Suddenly works of art assumed the status of relics or fetish-objects. There had been precedents. *Mona Lisa*, after her theft from the Louvre in 1911, became the world's best-known picture and she toured around Italy before returning to her home in Paris. Her name appeared on a range of products from purgative water to racehorses and cigars. She has been variously disfigured in replica – notably by Duchamp, of course – and traveled round the United States in 1963, where she was visited by 1,600,000 viewers. When she was taken to Tokyo and Moscow in 1974, more than two million people saw her. I do not know whether the "Mona Lisa Shop" established on the occasion in Tokyo to trade in Mona Lisa replicas – from posh framed reproductions through posters and plates to t-shirts – still exists, but any number of cafés, restaurants and even strip-joints all over the world still carry her name. Today she is shielded by bullet-proof glass and a cordon, a true relic. Increasingly vandal attacks on fetish-works, such as Picasso's *Guernica* or Michelangelo's *Pietà*, try the museum-visitor's patience and persistence.

All this has nothing to do with raising the level of taste, or with art historical scholarship, connoisseurship, or any of the other purposes for which earlier museums had been founded. In any case, very few of them are able to go on collecting the works of the great masters, since only very rarely do masterpieces appear on the market. As for antiquities, archeological sites which contain important deposits are very closely guarded in most countries, and very little of importance trickles out through unlicensed digs. New museums therefore have to look to living artists for their collections and exhibits, at the same time as their numbers and bulk increase. And since many of these new institutions are quite well-endowed, they have become the principal patrons of the artists in our time. To some extent, they also control the prestige of the artists, and inevitably the price-structure of the art market.

Furthermore, since any town which values its status needs a museum (or even better, several of different kinds), museums have become the very incarnation of urban pride, and because they are closely tied to prestige, they also need to be assertive. This is an important consideration when the authority of local government is being eroded for various reasons, and the centres of administrative power are no longer recognizable. Museums have therefore assumed some of the functions the town hall and the railway station had in the nineteenth-century town: Their cafés and shops have become convenient urban meeting places and they are also landmarks. The designs of these buildings and their locations have inevitably become crucial components of the city fabric.

Officials who run them are therefore prestigious figures. Even if they do not command the salaries of business executives, they have considerable sums at their disposal, and, of course, the holdings of the museums represent a vast capital outlay, which (if bought prudently) should be constantly rising in value. These officials are usually appointed by committees dominated by specialists – their peers – and thus form an important and international self-perpetuating caste.

The new religion the clerisy administers has an interesting and fully developed practice centered on the museum pilgrimage-visit; even if it has no foundation myth, no creed, no scripture (not even the Critique of Judgement!), it has developed quickly – in twenty or thirty years – and obviously fulfills a public need, as the long lines of people waiting to see major exhibitions attest. Sociologists have speculated about this crucial phenomenon of our time and the loss of "the great narratives" which provoked it without providing a satisfying answer. However, we have here three independent approaches to the problem of the museum in the city, each one formulated in very different circumstances. The most "natural" (in a way) is the Vitra Design Museum near Basel, which has grown out of the manufacturing process and the organization of the enterprise, since the company produces and markets furniture designed by some of the best architects and designers. Unlike most such entrepreneurs, Rolf Fehlbaum decided that the design of the individual buildings had to equal that of his products. What started as a private passion and involvement has become the Vitra trade-mark. Fehlbaum's account of the conflicts and tensions which this has involved is itself most instructive, both as a warning of the difficulties which anyone wishing to follow in his footsteps will inevitably meet and as an enthusiastic endorsement that it has all been worth it – not only for the enterprise but also for the patron personally.

Thomas Krens has been involved in the commissioning of some of the best living architects. And he had a precedent, in that the original building of the Guggenheim Museum by Frank Lloyd Wright is now – for all its disadvantages – one of the admired buildings of the century. His missionary endeavors in Austria and Italy have not yet borne fruit, but his mission to the Basques has resulted in a building which belongs to the same class as Wright's original masterpiece. Gehry's Bilbao Guggenheim is as much an urban intervention as the early nineteenth-century museums in Berlin, Munich and London, but with the added charge that it has an electrifying impact on the rather dour (and somewhat depressed) steelworks town.

Of course, this has posed another problem: can/should the building up-stage the exhibits? The exhibits are works of art — by definition. And the building itself — is that a work of art as well? Is it also on show? Should not the visitors preparing to admire the paintings and sculptures or the installations spare a moment to appreciate the building itself? There is another, ancillary question — implied, if not stated, in Frederick Smith's paper. That the building is a work of art he freely admits. In fact, I believe he made legal precedent (if not legal history) when he — and his architect — claimed that the percentage of the cost of a building which the state of California obliges patrons to spend on works of art in public commissions should be spent on the building proper, since the building is itself a work of art. There is, of course, something curiously philistine about a law which assumes that a work of art is necessarily something "added" to the building — as if the building itself could never be a work of art, though it must be admitted that in many cases art has little to do with building, even with museum buildings. Should a museum building not always have a claim to being a work of art? And there is another question: if the museum not only offers a home to works of art already in existence, but is also the promoter and evoker of new ones, should it just remain the place where such products are displayed, as they might be in commercial galleries, or should studios and workshops be included where the museum visitor can actually see the artist in operation? This is problematic in the case of conceptual artists, I admit, but even that should not be impossible. The late Georges Simenon used to advertise his books by sitting in his publisher's shop window in Paris, typing his next novel and smoking incessantly. Not every artist has the concentration or the speed such a procedure requires, of course — but some artists, those who work in large ateliers with several assistants, should have no such problem.

Be that as it may, museums have a great future. Their great financial resources, sometimes backed by governments, make them by far the most formidable body of auction-room bidders. Various forms of estate tax regulation ensure that the collections of private individuals or of families eventually pass into the public domain — which means museums again. The impoverished temples and churches of the old religions surrender the cult-statues and altar-pieces which are now national treasures and for which they cannot care with the "scientific" precision which modern conservation methods require. Increasingly all the dead art of past ages will be garnered into museums for its own protection.

All the main national museums have grown vastly since World War II, and they will continue to expand. Their place in the city has increased proportionately. In many cities (witness Bilbao!), they have become the principal public buildings and the principal meeting places of the population. They now have little or nothing to do with the exteriorless interrelated white boxes which my friend the curator aspired to direct — to which only a few visitors would go to experience the individual works of art aesthetically. The experience we now expect from the museum is of a different nature, but the buildings have become an important focus of public attention. This gives them a new role in the city and in the urban landscape, in fact in the culture of our time.

PARADIGM FOR A NEW RENAISSANCE

Frederick S. Smith

Frederick Samitaur Smith

We are currently developing a project in the city of Los Angeles which, in 1925, had a population of 500,000. Today 22 million people are living there. We have more Ph.D. recipients in Southern California than anywhere else in the U.S.A. We are the center for medicine, environmental studies, defense, communications, multimedia, and education. California has the seventh largest gross national product in the world, and Los Angeles, by itself, ranks eleventh.

These are various photographs of our buildings. You can see that we have started to interpose our vision on the city. Our proprietary interests, by their very nature, are public. Buildings, by their very nature, candidly express, for better or worse, externally the internal mechanism of a city's morality. This has been one of the basic premises of our development concepts.

If one seeks to redefine what a city is, one has to accept the fact that one's buildings must be interesting and challenging, and they must contribute to the cultural biology of your city. We believe that cities have a certain pulse, that they are organic.

We have selected to work in a sub-area of Los Angeles that is the eastern half of Culver City, which borders the northwest corner of South Central Los Angeles. Both of these areas suffered from benign neglect, and I chose to start our development where we did for political, social, philosophic, and economic reasons.

The scale at which we hope to work is global, though our approach is hemispheric, or local. We started in an industrial zone because it replicates abandoned industrial zones throughout the world. We presently have potential projects in Japan and Spain. In order to draw clients to our special vision, begun twelve years ago, we had to develop what we call "a catalyst for change."

In Los Angeles we do not really have historical wealth or aesthetics. We do not have a socialized government. We have no aristocracy. So we have to invent ourselves as we go

Aerial view, Culver City

View, Century City

Aerial view, INCE Project, 3960 INCE Blvd., Culver City

Surroundings, Los Angeles and Culver City

South Central, Los Angeles

Hollywood, Los Angeles

Aerial view, Culver City

along. In one sense this is extremely frustrating, and in another very invigorating. We fee
free to experiment. Intrinsic in our investment strategy, therefore, is a certain hubris tha
belies failure.

The paintings I am going to show you next are by Braque. They are bold intellectually
Madame Braque told me that socially their message was meant to convey that after Worlc
War I the world needed to be deconstructed and rebuilt in order to pursue some form o
political utopia.

Although visually pleasing, Braque's paintings did not achieve their ultimate end
which was to make people reevaluate their social and political attitudes. In a sense Braque
failed.

These examples of Braque's paintings are located far from the viewing public, in the
basement of the Louvre in Paris. I know this to be a fact because I spent twelve weeks in the
basement of the Louvre, viewing these works of art and others by Picasso and Juan Gris, and
I only got to see them because Braque's widow sought permission for me to do so.

Our idea since the very beginning has been to apply the same cubist aesthetics to urban
renewal that Braque and Picasso applied to painting. We wanted to deconstruct what it
meant to be an urban planner, an urban developer. We wanted to bring modern art out of
the museum and onto the street. Therefore, in order to define our utopia, we waged a full-
blown legal battle for a number of years in order to de-sanitize contemporary architecture,
to cleanse it of its Hellenistic mantle in order to get it accepted legally as an art form – a
contemporary art form.

The battle was extremely important, for architecture is not a utilitarian endeavor which
can be aptly executed by engineers as well as architects. Architecture is an art form, and it
must be executed by architects.

By establishing architecture as a legal art form, it became accepted as public art. This
meant that in real estate development terms, if a project had a certain aesthetic value, it
would be exempt from public art taxes because the architect was now an artist.

The reduction of the art fees meant that in purely real estate development terms the government would indirectly be forced to subsidize good architecture, under certain defined

Hayden Tract – 3535 Hayden Avenue, Culver City, Eric Owen Moss

Hayden Tract – 3535 Hayden Avenue, Culver City, Eric Owen Moss

conditions. And, if one's objective was to get art out of museum basements, then getting good architecture legally accepted as public art was essential.

In my opinion, the photos you are viewing now are good examples of architecture as art. Strange as it may seem, they have been shown in city planning commission meetings as well as on the walls of the Whitney Museum in New York City. Therefore, they subsequently met the city requirements for architecture as an art form.

What we have done by making architecture legally an art form on a quotidian level is to bridge the gap between those who do not view architecture as an art form, and those who do. Unlike Braque, we have made a deconstructive reality genuine. Our work is not in the basement of the Louvre; it is on the streets of South Central Los Angeles. That is something a museum director, no matter how arcane, can appreciate.

By the end of the year we will have completed the renewal of approximately 500,000 to 750,000 square feet (or 50,000 to 70,000 square meters). We bought these properties for approximately $10 a square foot (or $100 a square meter), and even after you reduce their worth for net-present values (considering the fact that our buildings are as yet only 75% leased), our project is now worth approximately $1,750 a square meter.

This is a proposal we made for an abandoned railroad track that runs through our area. It is the piece that we are hoping will knit the matrix together. It is called the Palindrome.

The genetic code for the Palindrome is a repetitive column and truss system, upon which are platforms that presently are amorphous in nature but will eventually support a variety of structural designs. These designs will turn our area into a haven for multimedia companies by the imposition of a park at grade, and, above the park, buildings that are sculptural in nature, and, therefore indicate prospectively a positive future.

By following the path of the railroad tracks, our idea is to make a surgical cut through a neighborhood that is currently a chaos of disparate elements: our neo-industrial buildings with high-tech users next door to run-down factories housing "sweat shops." The DNA of the Palindrome that will be inserted into this incision should heal and rejuvenate the entire area.

This next building is a very important building for me. It is 9046 Lindblade Street. In the very beginning, we did not know how to market our ideas. Unfortunately, due to my literary background, whenever I tried to explain my ideas to tenants or architects they were confused or categorically rejected my ideas, because they were literary in nature.

My ideas were outside the box. They were not linear. When I spoke to those first tenants and architects they would not listen to me, because their educational background did not permit it. They had to, later, physically see the work to understand it.

In my early days, I had become "animated" by nonlinear math. I had a background in physics. I knew about topographies and their meaning for all of us. But the architects I originally spoke to knew something about Hellenistic math, and nothing about nonlinear, fuzzy logic. They could not define something by what it was not. They knew nothing about negative numbers, and thus they saw structures as rigid forms that in an odd way had nothing to do with evolution, fluidity, atrophy, or the slow distillation of reality that occurs to objects as

Samitaur Building – 3455 S. La Cienega Blvd., Los Angeles, Eric Owen Moss

Samitaur Building – 3455 S. La Cienega Blvd.,
Los Angeles, Eric Owen Moss

Samitaur Building – 3455 S. La Cienega Blvd.,
Los Angeles, Eric Owen Moss

Samitaur Building – 3455 S. La Cienega Blvd., Los Angeles, Eric Owen Moss

Samitaur Building – 3455 S. La Cienega Blvd., Los Angeles, Eric Owen Moss

Interior view, Samitaur Building – 522 S. National Blvd., Culver City

rapidly as you create them. In other words, they were not informed about the importance of probability theory in terms of modern structures.

Their work was static and lacked incandescence. But they denied their intransigence. Their lack of incandescence was tied directly to the fact that their work was derivative and safe.

I had a knowledge of how computer chips were made and the calculus involved in their binary functions, which led to corollary actions and the architecture of inner space, i.e. the Internet. But I did not seem to be able to communicate this to the architects that I met.

Eric Moss was a tenant, and fortunately the day we met he was reading T.S. Eliot's *Four Quartets*, and we were able to discuss the structure, or architecture, of Eliot's poetry. By the time I met Eric I had ceased to speak to architects in literary or mathematical terms. I was by nature a symbolist. Therefore, in real time, I had been more or less reduced to expressing myself in poetic terms.

I told Eric I wanted to do a building based upon Cervantes' *Don Quixote*, and another one based on James Joyce's *Ulysses*. He loved the idea of creating formal episodic buildings that might in some vague, abstract way assimilate the episodic genius of Cervantes and Joyce.

So this is one of the first buildings we did. If you notice, there is a tilted wall (like a tilted windmill) that is supported by c-sections (c stands for Cervantes). There is a clock on the wall that does not work and represents the timelessness of the novel *Don Quixote*. We thought that the buildings were revolutionary. They became a gestalt of sorts — a self-generating image — a replicator of past promises of perception, past geniuses like Braque and Picasso, and Joyce and Cervantes, who understood antecedent histories and gave humanity new avenues to explore.

Young architects flocked to see 9046 under construction. It was leased before it was even completed. The building has received international recognition, and is one of the first buildings we were able to complete that people could immediately understand. In this building, I found the nomenclature to explain myself to tenants.

Here is another building: 8522 National Boulevard. It has received two national AIA awards.

It is actually a reconfiguration of the interior of another building — a barn. The literary reference for this building was James Joyce's *Ulysses*. Molly's soliloquy is a barnyard of sorts; a fitting allegory of sensuality, whose images defy space and time and achieve a certain universality.

And what 8522 National Boulevard does is present a fountain of kaleidoscopic images and forms that, although static in nature, stimulate the visitor's brain by implying that imbedded in all structure is a cryptogram of beauty and truth.

The detonator for 8522 might have been Joyce, but the building itself became a lighthouse — a beacon, embracing the future, built in a sincerely minimalist way, with great attention to detail.

The cornerstones of the building were elliptical geometries. The static forms of 8522 relentlessly indicate that freedom is there, no matter how inorganic the matter is. 8522 was a state of passage for us, a safe passage, that took us into the realm where true art dwells.

There is a story I would like to tell you: When I was 13 years old, I spent a week with my grandfather. He had just recently lost a friend, and he told me that I had to go along to his friend's funeral.

In preparation for the funeral, he bought me a brand new blue suit, a white shirt, and a lovely blue tie. Somehow in my mind I juxtaposed the fine clothes with the trepidation that I felt.

On the day of the funeral — apart from the black ribbon tied to the car's radio antenna, which blew with a ridiculous freedom in the summer breeze — nothing would have indicated where we were going. My grandfather was humming operatic arias. He had been a tenor in some unknown region north of Afghanistan.

However, when we walked through the massive metal doors of the synagogue, the air hung heavy with sweat and tears. Everyone's eyes were full of cockroaches.

My grandfather sang out in his tenor voice, "Why are we here?" And the congregation responded in unison: "We are here because someone has died, and it is his Judgement Day." Almost immediately, a crow appeared at the doorway to the temple. He turned his head from side to side.

My grandfather saw the crow. A pomade of lavender oil and rose water flattened his white tufts of hair, and his broad shoulders reminded me of a breathless Sisyphus, pausing before his stone.

The crow flew away when a stranger, the leader of the congregation, entered.

He wore a black silk jacket with a brown fur collar. His hat was sable. His eyes were colorless. That which went before him and behind him was silence.

He was a frail man, thin, and swollen at the neck, with a ruby vein that ran from his left eye to his left ear. His nose was broken at the nave and at the bridge. His tortoise-shell smile was toothless.

Swinging a finger across my chest in one swoop, he deftly cut the lapels of my new suit. My consciousness floated before me on the wings of a blue moth.

He then cut my grandfather's shirt, splattering blood across his bifocals. I had the sensation that snow was melting between my thighs.

Then he went up to the widow, who happened to be thirty years younger than her husband, and slashed her clothing – accidentally severing a shoulder strap of her dress.

I found her nudity to be disturbingly beautiful.

There was a certain rose hue to the widow's skin that looked as if Botticelli had painted it.

Almost immediately, several women covered the widow with a black veil; but her bare breasts shone with a transparency that bordered on winter mist.

We finally left the funeral, and later while having tea with my grandfather, I told Nathan that I had pretended that there were "eyes in my hands," as grandmother Esther had taught me. (She had said to me that when one awakes in the middle of the night, if one is frightened of the dark, just imagine there are eyes in your hands. Then you will be safe.)

Wiping a tear from my eye he said, "May our Father in Heaven grant you faith."

After removing a white handkerchief from my vest pocket to wipe a drop of blood from his bifocals, he asked, "Why did you see more in the widow's nudity than you saw in her bereavement?"

"How did you know that?" I asked.

"Your grandmother is thirty years my junior," he said.

There was a silence. Was he fifty years older than my mother? I asked myself. And I was thirty-six years younger than my mother was. In an instant I realized that he was eighty-six.

"You must never confuse responsibility and sorrow with lust," he said, touching a mole on my left hand. "Hitler did that."

So, why have I told you this story? Because I have met with many government officials, and in order to convince them to allow us to do what my wife and I wanted to do, I have had to remind them that there were crows at the door.

Many years ago, in order to punish us for being original, a planning commissioner demanded that we paint our building the color puce, a blatant reference to the color of vomit.

Change requires patience and a commitment to communicate one's ideas. What my wife and I try to focus on is the internal logic of our development. We try to keep the high quality work consistent and pure.

This leads me to the video I wish to show you.

I think that this video shows that everyone feels that our success is actually their success. Samitaur Constructs will fail, in Albert Camus' terms, if everyone does not take responsibility for what we do. Therefore, Conjunctive Points (the name of our urban experiment) is a compilation of numerous perspectives on aesthetics, art, politics, philosophy, economics, and social realism. Samitaur Constructs' greatest achievement is that through some form of democratic process, we have established a consensus for change in our neighborhood.

Conjunctive Points is not a Hegelian achievement. It is not a didactic of a single individual; it is a didactic formed out of the poetic convergence of many different people. There is no room in our project for an egotist. And the consensus that we have fought to develop is what Florence, Venice, and even the Taj Mahal is all about.

Now I am going to segue into how we created the capital for our business.

The presumed underpinning of modern advancement is money. With money, either through taxes or loans, it is assumed you can solve any problem (social problems as well); but sometimes old problems need new solutions.

For instance, the age-old adage that you cannot build buildings without money is not true. What one has to understand is that in order to do new construction, if one does not have the money, one sometimes needs to invent a new form of collateral.

The land I bought was polluted. It had sub-surface contaminants left by previous users, which meant that it could not be financed under ordinary banking policy. However, in the pollution I saw a new form of equity enhancement.

My buildings were located in an excellent geographic location in terms of their easy accessibility from all the important areas of the city, so I was confident that if they were recycled, I could develop the necessary cash flow to pay off a bank loan.

As the property stood, however, the best one could expect from it was an annuity. Because of the sub-surface pollutants, it could not be sold.

My theory was quite simple: I would absolve the previous users from further legal responsibility for the deterioration of the property if they would guarantee a bank loan for me with a Letter of Credit. Once the property was cleaned-up by the former users, and rented by me to new tenants, I knew that I could prove to a bank that it could be sold to third parties – and hence the Letter of Credit would dissolve.

However, it took me 24 months of negotiations to win the acceptance of my business plan. After two years of litigation with Hercules Powder Plastics, an international chemical company that employs 15,000 people and builds Saturn rocket engines, I got them to guarantee a bank loan for me.

What has occurred since at Conjunctive Points is the following: There were 700 jobs in our area when we began, and today there are approximately 4,500. The mean income has risen from $21,000 to $39,000, and from these jobs we have a worker-income capable of supporting 100,000 people. There had been very little money poured into the area; there is now over a billion dollars being invested annually. The police, who used to be fearful of patrolling the area, now cruise by every half-hour. Ambulance response time is 3 minutes instead of 30. The Fire Department is ranked in the top 20 in the nation. The homes that once sold for $100,000 or less now sell for $350,000. A Bear Stearns subsidiary called Constellation Ventures, with a capitalization of $102,000,000, is opening up an office in our buildings. This is essentially an investment bank that will invest in small start-up companies that employ 20–50 people. Conjunctive Points has created an incubator project – funded in part by the Psilos Group, the creators of ultrasound photography – whose sole operating mandate, in exchange for warrants, will be to supply emerging companies with centralized accounting and legal and marketing expertise.

In the process of developing the financial tools necessary to present our business plan to city officials, bankers, and individual investors, we discovered that many of these entities siphon funds from the poor urban areas of our city – the savings of lower-income families – and loan them to "safe" middle-class neighborhoods, in lieu of helping people in lower-income neighborhoods.

We have tried to show to the various layers of government, large financial institutions, and every title-holder who would listen, that they could not take $10,000,000 of savings or taxes from our community and distribute $8,000,000 of that money to a middle-class neighborhood, such as Brentwood, and only $2,000,000 to South Central.

With such institutions as Fannie Mae, we have tried to request that throughout the entire city the distribution of equity investment be balanced. We have tried to convince them that the creation of small businesses in poor neighborhoods is as important as giving money to poor people so they can buy homes – which they will ultimately lose if they do not have jobs.

On the left-hand side is an example of one of our completed buildings. On the right is the first step towards the completion of that project: the framing of a terrace.

I love this picture for the simple reason that there is a paint factory next door. This factory cannot move, because it cannot get an operating permit to work anywhere else in the city. This is due to the chemical nature of their work. That is a real problem for them, and a real advantage for us.

This means that in very practical terms they cannot move until we use our political clout or job-creation track record to help them relocate to another area, thereby giving us the opportunity to buy their property and redevelop it. So you see, this is another example of how to capitalize on a new form of collateral, and the collateral in this case is what is termed "social credits."

The tenant in one of our buildings next door to the paint factory is Eastman Kodak. But why did a company such as Kodak move next door to a paint factory?

Eastman Kodak's story is very interesting: Eastman Kodak employs 94,000 people around the world. But they are considered an institutional company because they will not give up a product line, namely, processed film – which is rapidly being eliminated by digital photography.

The people in the digital photography division of Eastman Kodak realized that the film processing end of the business, although passé, would never give them the marketing dollars necessary to expand Eastman Kodak's digital photography business.

They were losing a product line and a political battle within the corporation for marketing dollars. Therefore, they decided to move out of their high-rise in Hollywood, away from the film processing group – in part because we proved to them that their operating costs at Conjunctive Points would be 40% lower than at an ordinary high-rise building. And that therefore, they could apply those significant savings towards their marketing efforts.

Since the clientele they sought was going to be different from the customers of the film processing division, they knew that to move into our projects would bring them into contact with smaller companies that, like themselves, were directing their efforts towards the digitalization of education, communication, and multimedia. This would in turn give them a unique access to specialty customers.

Although I leased to them at a below-market rate, the trade-off was that I got their brand-identity, or their name in the project – and this was another form of collateral enhancement, since Kodak is the most recognized brand-name in the world. We cut a deal. We are dealmakers.

Because in essence they were a start-up business (even though they were within an institutional corporation) they understood and jumped at the chance to grow under the Conjunctive Points banner – and their sales have risen from $2,000,000 to $65,000,000 in three years.

Sony Entertainment Pictures has been a positive influence in our area. Their Image Works Division started in one of our spaces, and has grown from 65 to 1,000 employees in 4 years.

The project I am about to show you is the Box. Princeton and Yale Universities did a monograph on the Box, which was a soliloquy on the beauty of its construction.

However, my initiative for creating the Box was a totally different one, although I, too, find it very beautiful. Hidden within the abstraction of the design is a dome with a cube on top, and that is an inversion of the architectural basis for most mosques: cubes with domes on top.

The juxtaposition between the dome and the cube and how the dome and the cube are reversed, dissected, and sliced – and the fact that the Box exemplifies a traditional North African and Arabic form – expressed emphatically to me, in a very personal way, the potential future of the Moslem religion, and specifically, the future of African-Americans. In an odd way I saw the Box as an homage to Malcolm X, whom I profoundly respected.

I saw in the creation of the Box a symbolic icon for the elimination of racism and the distinctions of religion and color with regard to people of all nations. I did not see the Box as a purely architectural achievement. I could not separate it from its social context.

I think if I had regarded the Box as merely an architectural achievement – as purely a piece of architecture – or seen its meaning as only having something to do with a continuum of architectural evolution, I would not have authorized its construction.

For me to support good architecture, a symbiosis has to occur wherein form, purpose and function have to meld together seamlessly, and this is difficult to achieve. A developer has to define clearly the project's objectives and then take the talents of each individual on the team and intertwine them into a construct for the common good.

When one's private interests intersect with an artist's interests, or for that matter with the public's interests – such as the publication of the monograph by Princeton and Yale – something extraordinary can happen. The intersecting of these three interests releases a certain energy. It stimulates a new incentive that leads to action. It gives a new life to something old. You can see this when you walk into St. Peter's and are confronted with Michelangelo's *Pietà*. The *Pietà*, in a minimalist way, dominates the Basilica.

The invention of the Internet is equal to the invention of the printing press. If one is to comprehend today's world in a very real sense, then one has to understand that the Middle Ages is simultaneously co-temporaneous with our times. Right now, even as people race down the freeway in their Mercedes, the middle-class is acting like Benedictine monks – only they are sipping Moët & Chandon instead of brandy.

Most of us seem to be unable to recognize that the new technologies which are emerging daily in commerce, medicine and education will change our lives forever. Companies are growing from zero to $500,000,000 in two to three years: witness Amazon.com. The people who lack the skills necessary to understand this geometric growth, both in science and commerce, are going to be left behind.

To me, the Box conceptualized a sense of change, of urgency. It is a form that captures the state of human relationships of the moment (African-American human relationships). It is like the printing press or the Internet, which has just been invented.

About 3,500 tourists visit the Box each year. Tourism has become an ingredient of Conjunctive Points, and we are considering developing a hotel. People from incredibly varied backgrounds seem to be interested in what we do.

We are on the cusp of an analytic time when our imagination can be externalized by the imaging capabilities of the mathematical tools at our disposal. And soon, interior space will not be less important than exterior space. It will in fact be more important.

The foundations of structures will be based upon a calculus that will allow infinite variations. The use of literary and applied analogs to express the future is going to trickle away. Life in its infinite variety will become a symbol, and the future will be defined by poetry.

Let me show you again some photographs of 8522 National Boulevard which, although once based on James Joyce's *Ulysses* and certain elliptical geometries, is now a structure that has been in existence for eight years and has provided ample fodder for its tenants' imaginations. Therefore the statement of the building has been colored by their own creative interpretations of what we have done.

You cannot really see this building from the outside. It is more or less built like a military garrison since it was the first building we built in the area, and I was frightened by what was going on in the neighborhood. But when you walk inside, the building has a totally different appeal and structure. The interior of the building takes precedence over the exterior. It is therefore allegorically sensitive to cyberspace. In very real terms, in very real time, it is cyber.

Interior view, Hayden Tract, 3535 Hayden Avenue, Culver City, Eric Owen Moss

Interior view,
INCE Project,
3960 INCE Blvd.,
Culver City

Interior view, 3524 Hayden Avenue, Culver City, Eric Owen Moss

The Box, Culver City, Eric Owen Moss

Interior view, Office Building, 8522 National Boulevard Complex, Eric Owen Moss

The imposition of a small form on the surface of this old structure becomes a cursor that pulls you inside the building, occupied by engineers who, until recently, headed up Hughes Aircraft Company's holographic projection division. Here you have an exterior form emanating from the interior, suggesting a company's function. This facility was built for a totally new clientele. These gentlemen are inventing search engines for the Net.

Here you have a photo of Gregory Hines. He is our client, along with Janet Jackson, the Joffrey, the Houston Ballet, the Ballet Nacional de Cuba – many major dance companies use our center to hold auditions and to rehearse. Baryshnikov was in our studio recently. This dance center is our first step towards integrating the arts and science.

In conclusion, in the early years of our work there were riots in Los Angeles. The year was 1992, when my wife and I actively began our commitment to change: to engage ourselves in a manner that fit the social philosophy expressed by Albert Camus in his rebellious newspaper, *Combat*.

We had a very simple theory that if you created jobs where the poor lived, you could eliminate civil unrest and poverty.

It all began with the fact that I had an art collection and I exchanged it for real estate. I have often thought that if I had approached certain important painters, collected their work, or had an auction on their behalf, I could have begun a lot faster than I did. For every painter who suffers over the human condition, there is always one who wants to do something about it. They would have supported me.

William Faulkner, in a well-known eulogy to his dog, expresses my ideals the best. He said, "I shed tears about human suffering, but my dog did something about it."

In *The Last of the Just* Andre Schwartzbart has his main character howl like a dog in an open field, when he reaches the conclusion that he has to return to the concentration camp from which he has escaped, in order to die with those he loves.

In many ways it is a dog's life.

Sometimes life requires that we remain loyal to our principles even when the principles themselves seem to be without meaning or purpose; and far beyond any religious proscriptives, we must obey our own personal commandments.

In Los Angeles, on the night of a thousand separate fires, my wife and I were horrified. We decided that we did not want to be academicians, nor did we want to engage in cocktail talk. The political and philosophic polemic of our time did not interest us. What we wanted to do was to create a paradigm for a new renaissance.

And we knew that the people with whom we would be working would be stake-holders who would last for a while, and would not be fearful of pursuing their dreams, until they passed the baton forward to the next generation of poetic yeomen.

But what is most important to us is that we have done 27 projects, and the Culver City Boys, our local street gang, have never "graffitied" any of them. They respect our buildings as a sign of hope. So urban development is a symbol of promise – at least in our neighborhood. It should be in yours as well.

Lindblade Tower, Culver City, Eric Owen Moss

Gary Group Office Building, Culver City, Eric Owen Moss

Building, 3535 Hayden Avenue, C.C. 90230, Culver City

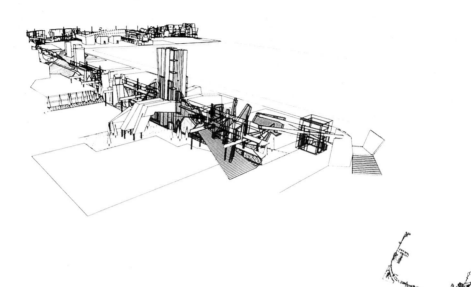

Sketch, Future Project, Culver City, Eric Owen Moss / Samitaur Constructs

Model, Future Project, Los Angeles, Eric Owen Moss / Samitaur Constructs

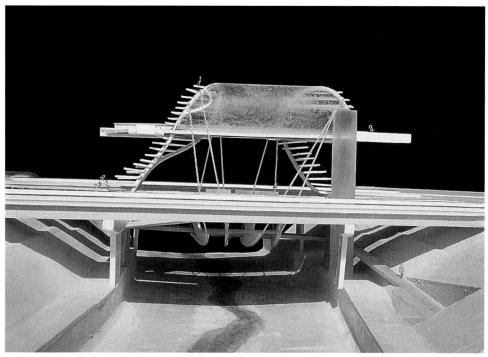

Model, Future Project, Los Angeles, Eric Owen Moss / Samitaur Constructs

Model, Future Project, Los Angeles, Eric Owen Moss / Samitaur Constructs

DEVELOPING THE MUSEUM FOR THE 21ST CENTURY: A VISION BECOMES REALITY

Thomas Krens

Thomas Krens

It is wonderful to be here in Vienna with so many old friends. A lot has been written about the recent developments in Bilbao and the Guggenheim Museum there. For many years before that, however, our focus was in Salzburg and here in Vienna, working with Hans Hollein, and it was here that the notion for an international museum began developing. So I have very fond memories of this place, and I am mixing, I suppose, these comments on a recent history and projections into the future with some nostalgia, because I am sure you'll see, as I tell the story, how this touches on many things that began here in Austria and in fact here in Vienna.

Peter Noever focused a bit on the title of this talk, *Developing the Museum for the 21st Century: A Vision Becomes Reality*. Now, I am not entirely sure whether I want to claim that this is a vision becoming reality, or that it defines anything about the 21st century. What I would like to do is to take you through the thinking that produced that outcome. I do not think there is any lesson that can be distilled from that. So much of that was circumstantial, and so much had to do with events and individuals and activities that took place.

You know, projects and accomplishments are developed by people, people's ideas are always changing, always in formation, and from time to time special things can happen. I have the good fortune to be involved, I think, in something that was, and perhaps is, happening. Let me now try to take you through a story that I think will illuminate something about what we are doing and perhaps de-mystify some of the apprehension that it seems to generate in the press. I do not think that the Guggenheim's activities are that threatening. I think they are rational, logical, and open to all kinds of collaborations. To that extent, at least, I do see it as a strategy in general for museums in the future.

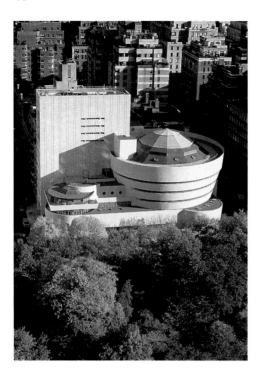

The Solomon R. Guggenheim Museum,
New York, Frank Lloyd Wright

The photographs that you see here are the Guggenheim Museum – you probably know i
– which was designed by Frank Lloyd Wright in the 1940s and built in 1959. This was th
shape and frame of the Guggenheim about ten years ago when I first arrived there. The char
acter of the institution was defined by the collection in the building.

Ten years later there is a new image of the Guggenheim Museum. That is the Guggen
heim Museum in Bilbao. Some people are claiming that it is one of the great buildings of th
20th century. I think it is. I think that Frank Gehry's achievement with it is quite special an
it has some unusual components, and perhaps these two images capture its silhouette, its pro
file, and the picture on the right gives you some sense of its scale. One of the 19 galleries i
the museum is about 134 meters long. That sculpture by Richard Serra is a large work, i
weighs 176 tons. The sculpture by Claes Oldenburg is about 20 meters wide and *Barge*, a larg
work by Robert Rauschenberg, is about five meters high and about twelve meters in diamete
I draw your attention to these three works because each of them existed before the museun
was built. So, in many ways you can see that the museum is a response to a set of condition
that, I believe, existed in the art world. And what we were trying to do was to respond t
those conditions.

However, my ideas about the Guggenheim Museum, and about museums in general, actu
ally had a fairly long incubation period. Before I came to the Guggenheim in 1988, I spen
almost 20 years teaching at the Art Department of Williams College. I suppose it was a typ
ical academic experience that was somewhat isolated from the rest of the world, or so i

Aerial view, Guggenheim Museum Bilbao, Frank O. Gehry

Interior view, Guggenheim Museum Bilbao, Frank O. Gehry

seemed. Most of the discourse tended to take place on a fairly theoretical level, and in tha process of thinking about art from an academic and even philosophical perspective, I begar to think about museums and why I found them disappointing. When I say I found them dis appointing I would use museums as a teaching tool; we were about three hours north of Nev York City by car and we would take students to New York to the Metropolitan Museum anc the Museum of Modern Art, or the Whitney Museum, or the Guggenheim Museum, both to see exhibitions and to see works of the permanent collection. And I began to be aware of cer tain things about museums. One is that it was almost impossible to find the work you wanted to see, particularly if you were working in the modern or contemporary period. One of the reasons for this was the fact that the museums' collections were much larger than thei ability to show. If you wanted to see a given work by Ellsworth Kelly, for example, it wa almost impossible to do so without making special arrangements. I sort of wondered abou this; what were museums for – particularly modern and contemporary museums – if they really could not respond broadly to the needs of the public? And that is just one example.

So I began to think about museums as an 18th-century idea, the idea of the encyclope dia, a sort of systematic way of looking at the universe, characterizing works of material cul ture fundamentally by chronology, by geography and biography. I saw them in a 19th-century box and the box was the extended palace, a series of rooms. Prior to 1879, the Louvre was a private house, and it only became a public museum with a sense of incipient democracy developing in France. This whole notion of making objects of material culture available to the population at large is very recent, in historical terms.

And the box, the frame for showing this, is essentially a room, a large room of a scale between this scale and a living room. And somehow, as you began to think about it, you real ized that this notion of the art museum had become obsolete sometime toward the middle o the 20th century – in many ways, because of what the museum could not respond to. My for mative years from an art historical perspective focussed on movements after pop art – such a op art, minimalism to a certain extent, environmental art, performance art – and the museun seemed hopelessly out of date to respond to these cultural needs. In other words, art had gone someplace else, and the museum was not following or did not seem to be following. So to me there was a fundamental question of the relevance and definition of the institution. Was the museum supposed to reflect culture, or was it to be a treasure house that collectec objects and sometimes made it difficult for the public to see these objects? So I think tha there was what I would call a philosophical anxiety, or perhaps even a philosophical crisis about the definition of art museums in future.

When I first came to the Guggenheim the simple task was to make a list of the objective for the institution. It had some assets, as I called them – bad choice of words, perhaps, bu assets nevertheless. We had a great collection, identity in our architecture, two great loca tions, and a fairly positive image around the world – partly because of the architecture. And we did have international presence, although it was tiny, with our museum in Venice, which was acquired in the 1970s. But the question was, what could we try to do? First of all anc most important, strengthen the collection. And the permanent collection of the Guggenheim has been enormously strengthened over the past ten years. In that time, we probably acquired close to 1,000 works of historic and important dimension. In many ways the development of the collection was very much linked to the energy that was being generated by the program and the building, and I will talk a bit about that as I go on.

We also saw a structural definition or redefinition of art museums. Another question was: If the traditional model did not work, what was the new model? To tell you the truth, I did not know the answer then, and I do not know the answer now, except that you find solutions by experimentation. And you find solutions by a rational process of trying to engage the best artists, the best architects, the best curators, the best people, to work with you. What helped motivate us was a conscious awareness that these people and these alliances were going to be part of the future of the institution.

This meant developing the collection, developing the museum, internationally strengthening it financially, making alliances that would benefit the institution and preserve its traditional values over the long run. What motivated this whole enterprise was a reading of the original charter of the Solomon R. Guggenheim Foundation, which was written in 1937. It talked about developing a collection, it talked about building museums and even used the plural, although I am sure that Solomon R. Guggenheim was not aware that we would have a museum in Bilbao one day. But the Guggenheim charter used the plural and it talked about an educational function and it talked about an institution that should by definition remain at the cutting edge of its field. So it seemed to me that all these things were clearly mandated. The hard part, of course, was to try to figure out how that would work.

Where are we ten years later? Just to set the stage, from 1989–92 we built this building to take some of the pressure off the Frank Lloyd Wright building and completely restored the Frank Lloyd Wright building on the inside and outside, and we opened up spaces that had been denied even when it was originally constructed because many changes were made after Frank Lloyd Wright's death but before the museum opened that compromised its original intention. We supplemented our exhibition programming activities with a second site in SoHo in New York City. We gradually, over the last 20 years, continued to build an expanded museum in Venice. We integrated the Mattioli Collection, which has been placed on a ten-year long-term loan to the Guggenheim. It is one of the great Italian futurist collections, with about 36 paintings, and we integrated it within the Peggy Guggenheim Collection. We have opened up new permanent collection space, we have added rooms in the buildings on the other side of our courtyard behind Peggy's original palazzo and this year we should have more than 300,000 visitors to this tiny little place that ten years ago was enjoying only about 45,000 visitors. It seems to be generating the kind of support we need to operate – through its program, and I think a responsible approach to developing the collection and its fundamentally permanent collection there. Indeed, even ten years ago, thinking that expanding internationally made sense, we began to negotiate for this building at the bottom of the Grand Canal. And we never give up. Ten years later, I have just had a meeting with Massimo Cacciari, the mayor of Venice, this Monday, and we signed an agreement for the creation of a Guggenheim

Museum of Modern and Contemporary Art in Venice. Of course, this is Italy, this may take little while. The larger part of the building is still part of the Dogana, a customs house. The agreement does include provisions for negotiating with the patriarch of Venice, and the City has just allocated three million dollars for a new building in Mestre to move the custom house out, so it is likely to take about two years. Our projection now is that by the end of 2002 or 2003, we will be seeing another active space.

Of course the museum in Bilbao, which I will talk about, was followed by a perhaps even more surprising event, a tiny little space on Unter den Linden in Berlin. It is only 400 square meters, it is really just one room, but in a wonderful location across from the library between the Brandenburg Gate and the Museum Island, near the State Opera. This was a perfect location for us to have a different kind of activity. It is not a museum; it is a collaboration with Deutsche Bank, where part of our requirement for participation was the ability to commission two major works a year, with a very significant budget, for a five-year period. Berlin is very important as a programming site for small exhibitions but this is also a way to continue to develop the collection.

In the past five years the Guggenheim has still continued to do what it is known for. We show exhibitions. We now organize something like 16 exhibitions a year that travel around the world. In the past five years, the Guggenheim has organized exhibitions that have been at 95 museums in Asia, Europe, and the United States. We continue to develop our collection and have great depth that ranges from early Picasso to Brice Marden and Elsworth Kelly and Robert Ryman and minimalists that came with the Panza Collection. We have also broken with tradition in recent years by wandering outside our field. Last February we opened an exhibition called *China 5000 Years* at the Solomon R. Guggenheim Museum that was curated by Sherman Lee, the former director of the Cleveland Museum of Art, a museum director for 25 years, probably the greatest U.S. authority on Chinese art. The quality of the exhibits was so extraordinary that even the curators at the Metropolitan Museum were forced to admit that such a dazzling display of Chinese art has never before been seen in the United States.

Two years earlier, in 1996, we did an exhibition with the Royal Academy in London on the art of Africa, and after China we opened an exhibition at the Guggenheim called *The Art of the Motorcycle*, which Frank Gehry installed by cladding the entire interior of the Guggenheim in highly reflective stainless steel. The show featured 114 motorcycles from 1868 to 1998, one a year with a very strict standard of selection. This exhibition, unhappily perhaps, was the best-attended exhibition on a daily basis that we have ever had. In 77 days we drew 325,000 people, and I can tell you that they were not motorcycle riders.

Now, what does all of this mean and what do you conclude from it? Well, in Peter Noever's introduction he mentioned the Guggenheim threat and the danger of combining art with commerce. I do not know if we indulge in commerce per se. The success that we might have in raising money is not necessarily commercial, and when people sometimes accuse me of focusing unnecessarily on financial issues, I point to the Metropolitan and say: Well, th

Metropolitan has 34 stores and does a 125 million dollar-a-year retail business. Who is in this for the money? And they have a 900 million-dollar endowment. Clearly with numbers like that we live in a world that has different levels of reality. And I am not so sure that there is any perfect definition of what an art museum should be, but I can make an attempt at defining it, first by acknowledging its functions. Our function is collection, conservation, historical analysis, education, and entertainment. And since culture does have a political and an economic dimension, we also have to think about what it is that makes the museum a successful enterprise. A good location is important. Vienna is a great place for an art museum, so is New York. And the right location in those cities is important. Great collections are necessary, great architecture helps, special exhibitions, I would say, are necessary. You have to have shopping opportunities or people will not come back, they have to eat, and high technology can help explain things. When I mean high technology I also probably mean low technology as well. We have to tell better stories in the museum. We have to be able to conceptualize and contextualize, because people who come to art museums are a very demanding audience. We also felt that there is an economy of scale through having museums that are linked internationally.

How did all this develop? The Guggenheim international project began in Salzburg, and that is where it really became a reality. I learned a number of things through this process. Number one: The architecture was given to me. I came to the project late in the game; Hans Hollein and his team had already developed this rather extraordinary design for the Mönchsberg, and I thought that the notion of an art museum that had a 60-meter rotunda inside the Mönchsberg and a museum that had no exterior was about the sexiest thing I had ever heard of. When you looked at it and you took the museum apart, you found that it had spaces that respected the needs of presentation in a conventional way. But it also had spectacular spaces that would allow you to present art that until then had been regarded as somehow difficult and beyond the reach of most museums. So Salzburg was important to me because of the lessons I learned about museum architecture.

However, it was also important because of the lessons of our politics. I came to understand that there is a window of opportunity in projects of this dimension. And when we made the presentation, the approach at the time I believe was mandated essentially by political considerations. This is my belief. I think that in 1989, with the increasing liberalization of the Soviet Union, Austria saw itself as a member of the EEC, as a country that would have increasing exchange with Eastern Europe. I think we came to the attention of the Austrian side through a coalition of private individuals and government officials. And essentially we said: If you build this building there will be an economic return in jobs, in turnover and in tax revenues, and that probably in a period of around ten years the building would pay for itself.

We developed that argument in the feasibility study for the Salzburg project and let me tell you a fact: The Guggenheim Museum in Bilbao just completed its first year of operation on October 19. We had 1.385 million visitors in the first year. The economic impact was

Model, Guggenheim Museum Salzburg, Hans Hollein, 1989/90

31,000 million pesetas – or translated into dollars it was 220 million dollars – for the local economy, and that is about two billion Austrian schillings. That means the building will pay for itself in four years, in terms of the total investment that has been made by the local Basque government. The whole transformation that has taken place in the Basque Country in the last year has been absolutely remarkable. Our financial planning is anticipating a rate of 895,000 visitors for the next couple of years and I think with strong programming we will probably get around 1.1 million, maybe 1.2 million, maybe even more. I think that the lesson here is that culture does have a political and an economic dimension and it is crazy not to think about it that way because it gives you a hold on the process that can be used to generate resources. My point here is again that from my perspective Salzburg was where we had a chance to develop these attitudes and to present those conclusions in an even more forceful way.

Sadly, Salzburg did not happen, and it was clear by early 1991 that it had not so much to do with a decision taken against developing a project in Salzburg but rather simply nothing was happening. And I had my agenda. The Guggenheim could be perhaps aware of what was taking place in various parts of the world, but we certainly were not in control of that and we had things we had to accomplish. By that time we were definitely interested in developing other international locations, but when the Basques first came to us, I said absolutely no. I just could not see the Guggenheim being in Bilbao, because I was sort of in love with Salzburg. I mean it had music and it was a nice place to go, it was in Central Europe and it was in Austria, it was close to Vienna – you know, all these advantages.

Bilbao had none of those features and none of those characteristics. I had never even been there and I did not want to go either. I went out of an obligation to Carmen Gimenez and some friends in Madrid, and I fully believed that I was going to really say no. The first time I was ever in the Basque Country it was on this visit, and it was on April 9, 1991, and when I arrived there they had a helicopter at the airport and a red carpet. I was surprised, I thought a government official was on the plane, but alas it was for me, and here is a much younger Guggenheim director circa 1991 getting in this helicopter, and flying to Vitoria, the capital of the Basque Country, for a meeting with the president of the Basque Country, and I told him point blank that I did not think the Guggenheim should be in Bilbao because it had a bad image. And I added, whether it is true or not, when I think of the Basque Country, I think of terrorism and jai alai.

And he said, "Well, you made a mistake, but put that aside for a moment, that is not the question that I have. The question that I have is: What would it take?" We just came off the disappointment of the Salzburg project, the fact that it was not happening, and I knew exactly what it would take. In fact I knew it better than I had when we began the Salzburg project. So I said, "Well, it would take 150 million dollars to build the museum. It would take 100 million dollars to support the museum with an endowment that would generate 10 million dollars," and I threw in some other things that were not part of the Salzburg project, like 50 million dollars for acquisitions, 20 million dollars for the Guggenheim, selection of the architects and control of the process, selection of the site, and total design and administrative control. I mean, I had no expectations at all – I was not trying to convince him to do this. And they said, "Yes." Just like that, right there, on the spot. I mean, it was just like that. I basically said: It will cost you 320 million dollars to do the project overall, if you want to look at it that way. And he said, "Fine," and I was apprehensive at that point. Apprehensive, because I was still not sure about the place, and that also began an interesting transformation for me.

In the end I realized that in many ways I had found the perfect place for something like this to happen, for many reasons. It had to do with deep-seated political reasons that I could not even begin to guess at in terms of the relationship between the Basque Country and the rest of Spain. It had to do with financial and economic reasons. I had not been aware until then that in 1977, with the death of Franco and the restoration of the Spanish Republic, the Basques had negotiated fiscal autonomy; they do not pay taxes to the Central Government and they have the highest per capita GNP, therefore they are capable of raising that kind of money in the world financial markets as a matter of public debt finance. Moreover, they were already embarked on a massive two-billion-dollar infrastructure development project for the Basque Country that included a new subway system that was designed by Norman Foster and opened in 1995. It was 32 kilometers of subway and it cost about 950 million dollars. There is a new airport that opens next year designed by Santiago Calatrava that is costing 400 million dollars. James Stirling was designing the train station, essentially a retro-fitting of the train station – a project that seems to be temporarily on hold. A new convention center with a 2200-seat opera house, a 600-seat theater, five 1500-seat theaters, and ten 100-seat conference rooms opens, I think, next month. And Cesar Pelli has designed a master plan for a business development on the property adjacent to the art museum. All of this was more or less under way, and it went a

Aerial views, Guggenheim Museum Bilbao, Frank O. Gehry

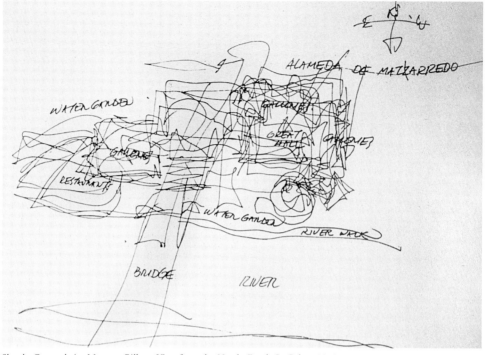

Sketch, Guggenheim Museum Bilbao, View from the North, Frank O. Gehry, 1991

long way toward changing the perspective of the Guggenheim trustees about the possibilities for a museum in Bilbao.

Part of the deal was that they had agreed to let me select the site. And I said, "You can choose the architects, but I'm going to pick three that I think that we can work with."

The site is marked by this big bridge that comes down out of this very steep hill that is actually in the city, and it connects to the airport on the other side of the city. You come into the city right down to this major street which intersects with what is called the Gran Via. This whole area was part of the original port of Bilbao. The actual city is about six kilometers upriver from the Atlantic Ocean, and this picture shows the deepwater estuary and a draw-bridge, so you can actually see the ocean-going boats coming through under this drawbridge, under this tall bridge and as far as there. This was still a railhead for shipping, there are four shipping warehouses here, with all kinds of cranes typical of an active port facility. I saw this for the first time from a helicopter. It was that same helicopter that carried me around. And I just looked down and said, "How about that down there?" And they bought it. A couple of months later it was in private hands, so the site was literally selected and developed before the architects were selected.

I felt that we had to work with three architects, but architects that we felt had a rationale, and that we had experience with. Frank Gehry, whom I have been working with in Mass MoCA in the United States, was one of my choices; Arata Isozaki, who is doing the Guggenheim Museum in SoHo, was another; and Coop Himmelb(l)au – Wolf Prix, my great friend, and Helmut Swiczinsky – were the two architects from Austria who came. We had a rather unusual competition which was: Each of the architects was given one site visit, 10,000 dollars and three weeks to design the building. And there were no real requirements.

I asked Heinrich Klotz, a good friend of mine who had just left the directorship of the Architekturmuseum in Frankfurt, to be the referee for the jury. The way we structured it was that I picked the three architects, but I was not a member of the jury. The members of the jury were Carmen Gimenez and three government officials from the Basque Country. We conducted the jury on 21 July 1991. Keep in mind that I went to the Basque Country for the first time on April 9 and three months later we had already selected an architect, acquired a suitable plot, and moved the project along.

As you can see, Frank's first drawing captures something of the kind of avuncular feeling of the Guggenheim in Bilbao. And this is the Coop Himmelblau's presentation. When I had seen some elements of their design in a competition for the ZKM – the Zentrum für Kunst und Medientechnologie in Karlsruhe – I fell in love with their work. I did not know that at the time, although I had seen some small projects of theirs here in Vienna when we developed the feasibility study. You can see that the bridge was already part of the site, and one of the requirements of the program was that the building had to be on both sides of the bridge and occupy this site. I was somehow captured by these notions of the cubes that would glow in the dark, and the whole series – this is really almost just a translucent surface skin that contained galleries of different shapes and dimensions, because the space here is really quite large. Quite an adventurous design.

This design almost won but did not in the end. There was a very spirited discussion between Frank's and Wolf's designs. Another drawing of Frank's shows how the bridge is integrated into it – of course this is later when the building was already constructed. I did not bring along any slides of the first model, but you could certainly see the site, the railhead, and the fact that this whole area – which is now absolutely central to the re-development of Bilbao – was literally not part of anybody's thinking at that time, which seemed to me to be absolutely surprising.

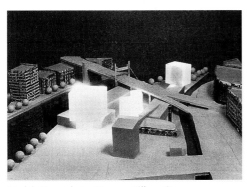

Model, Guggenheim Museum Bilbao, Coop Himmelb(l)au

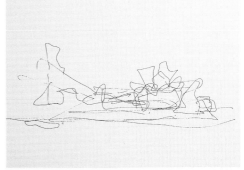

Sketch, Guggenheim Museum Bilbao, View from the North, Frank O. Gehry, 1991

Thus began a rather extraordinary process because, as I mentioned earlier, we had virtually complete control over the process. Frank and I just met every two weeks for two year and that was it. I mean it was not more complicated than that. We never took the designs to anybody. There was only one iron rule, which was that you could never go over the budget And there was always somebody from the Basque Country sitting in on the design meetings taking notes and never saying a word and working with Frank's people on the budget. As a result we finished this building on time about one percent under the budget, which is quit remarkable.

The design process was extraordinary. It started out in a very casual way where Frank would make models and models and models. Of course it helped that all these things were just pieces of twisted paper with some scotch tape and some pins holding them all together. But this was the beginning of a process using a computer-assisted design program developed by the French Aerospace Industry for designing Mirage fighters to transform these curved cardboard paper forms into a working drawing. Not the normal thing that architects generally use. But what it allowed you to do was to create the structures for these vast curved metal surfaces. And one of the tests of this is that there are 11,000 steel structures, steel members, beams, inside this Guggenheim Museum in Bilbao and no two are the same. In other words, there is no bull order in here because everything is at a slight curve or an angle, and yet with that high level of complexity because of the introduction of amazing technology. I have never seen this any place else before or heard that architects worked like this with this level of technology. Basically we were able to take a liberally funded project, make the right level of financial investment in the technology, and produce a highly innovative, almost brilliantly innovative and highly efficien re-solution. I think that kind of combination is one of the most remarkable aspects of the whole project. But that was the technical side of it.

One of the other aspects had to do, you might say, with what I call the conversational side. From the beginning, when we started talking about the program, I talked about the building in terms of Chartres Cathedral. I said that I wanted people, when they saw this building, to have the same reaction at the end of the 20th century and the beginning of the 21st century that somebody who approached Chartres Cathedral in the 15th century would have had, whether that was a pope or a peasant. You sort of come out of the countryside and all of a sudden there it is – high technology. That is the kind of response I wanted. Well, that is a grand sort of analogy to invoke, but what is it going to look like?

Early on we got into this discussion about searching for metaphors. And I can remember every once in a while Frank would call me up and say, I got another one. But we boiled it down and one of them was Fritz Lang's film *Metropolis*, sort of the impression of a drawing from the conception of the great city in the 1930s, and that verticality part of the element of the high level walkways that unfortunately you cannot see so well in this picture of Bilbao. But the walk ways that circle the major atrium of the Guggenheim Museum Bilbao are an ocean of high bridges and elevated walkways soaring in space – Fritz Lang's *Metropolis* was a very consciou selection as an image metaphor. Another one was Brancusi's studio. We looked at books of Brancusi's studio to try and find counterpoints that were developed, and you can see this in

Interior view, Guggenheim Museum Bilbao, Frank O. Gehry

Interior view, Guggenheim Museum Bilbao, Frank O. Gehry

Deutsche Guggenheim Berlin, James Rosenquist, *The Swimmer in the Econo-Mist*, 1998

Interior view, Guggenheim Museum Bilbao, Frank O. Gehry

photographs of the interior of the museum with these wonderful white kinds of curvilinear shapes that have sometimes been likened to Marilyn Monroe's dress, but they actually came out of Brancusi's studio at the turn of the century. A third metaphor were the sails of the ship because Bilbao is a seaport. Frank was very conscious of wanting to have it invoke the water, so the sails of the ship appeared as a kind of repeated image in metaphor, both on the inside throughout and endlessly. And finally a rock quarry with these various layers and platforms of carving stone, a blond stone out of a rock quarry in Indiana. These four images together comprised the developments of the plans. We began to develop this in September 1991, and ground was broken in October 1993. Thus we had two years for the design development, to indulge this fantasy. And it was literally a fantasy.

The design process was one amazing component. Another amazing component to me was the political process because even though we came to an agreement, and even though we had signed a preliminary agreement, we all predicted that we would have to sign agreements at three stages. We called them the development agreement, the management agreement, and the operation agreement. The key one was the first one, the development agreement. And this is where the project begins to show parallels, a little bit, to perhaps what befell Salzburg, because I am fond of saying now and I also believe this to be true, that if we had started this project four months later it would have never happened, because the political support for this which for complex reasons was very strong in the summer of 1991 was rapidly eroding through the fall of 1992 as we were approaching the signing date for the development agreement, which would be the first big transfers of money. It was an incredible moment. I remember that the date for the signing was the 13th of December 1991 and at that time we got a message in New York that they wanted to postpone this until sometime in 1992. If this had happened, we would have never seen the project, because what it meant was that you went into a completely new fiscal year with respect to budget allocations. And there was opposition to this project – and it was significant political opposition, not on a cultural level or even an economic level, but simply because it had been introduced by another side.

At that time we needed a white knight. And my white knight was, at that time, the Italian Foreign Minister, Gianni De Michelis. Since then he has had a rather difficult time in Italian politics, but in 1991 he was on top of his game. He was the foreign minister of Italy, and Italy was the head of the EEC and Gianni De Michelis talked about Europe in terms that are only being realized now. He also happened to be a trustee of the Guggenheim Foundation. When they tried to postpone the signing from December into the next year, I called Gianni in Rome and I said I need your help, I need somebody who has the stature to represent the Guggenheim so they cannot change the date, and he said he would come to sign the contract on behalf of the Guggenheim, which he did.

The long and the short of it is that it was Gianni De Michelis who signed the final agreement on behalf of the Guggenheim on December 13, 1991, and that launched the process in a way that was irrevocable. Because the first big transfer of funds, the first bond issue, was undertaken, the President of the Basque Country then signed a renewed agreement in February 1992 in the presence of the mayor of New York City, at that time David Dinkins, the mayor of Bil-

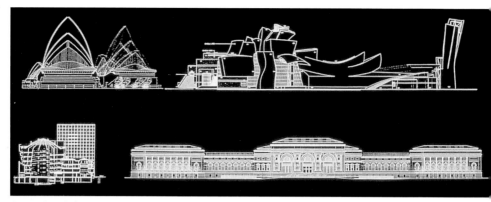

Comparison Sydney Opera House, Guggenheim Bilbao, Guggenheim New York, Metropolitan Museum New York

bao, the president of the regional council of the Basque Country, the chairman of the Guggenheim, and President Ardanza.

We had a partnership that led to five years of unrelenting criticism in the press – this project was savaged up and down everywhere all over. It had no supporters. It was an orphan except it had a contract and moved forward on the strength of its contract. For four years we existed in this kind of weird limbo of having nobody in favor of the project.

Guggenheim Museum Bilbao, Jeff Koons, *Puppy Dog*, 1997

Another interesting thing about the project was the degree to which we engaged artists at a very, very early state of the process. We had many projects under way with Jeff Koons, but one of the most successful was the realization of his *Puppy Dog*, which was done for the 1987 Documenta. Here is another issue where the politics were intense: when I first proposed Jeff Koons. This is right at the height of Jeff Koons' and Cicciolina's fame and so the government was not receptive to a commission by Koons, and now this is the prime site in Bilbao for confirmations and marriage ceremonies. Everybody comes here to have their photographs taken in front of the Jeff Koons *Puppy Dog* and it has become the feature of Bilbao. We did major commissions. This is actually a very huge room about 16 meters high, by Sol LeWitt, this is another very tall room, a commission of Jenny Holzer. We even commissioned dead artists; we negotiated with the estate of Yves Klein to build a fire fountain that was originally conceived in 1960 and installed at significant expense in front of the museum. These works by Jim Dine are very large, probably about ten meters high. Francesco Clemente was engaged to develop a series of 17 paintings just for a single room.

As part of our collaboration with Deutsche Bank we commissioned a large work by Jim Rosenquist in three panels: one panel was 32 meters long, one panel 15 meters long, and one panel was six meters long. The piece was presented for the first time at the Deutsche Guggenheim Berlin, but will now travel to Bilbao to be shown on a single wall for the first and only time. We planned galleries in developing the building program – and this was the lesson that we took from the Salzburg project. We wanted a building that had galleries that were equally hospitable to these huge works of art, on the one hand – and you see the long gallery, and there is also a tall Anselm Kiefer Gallery where we brought six major paintings by Kiefer – but we also had gallery spaces that were intimate spaces where you could show drawings by Picasso, or delicate sculptures. We found innovative ways to bring natural light into the space. These are two galleries, one on top of another, but the one on the upper floor has this chimney around it – we call it a chimney, because it allows natural light to come down through here and into the gallery below. So there are some very, very classical elements to this space. This space is almost square, rectilinear doors, and yet you have this donut or chimney in the middle of the very classical gallery that is early 20th-century art, and then you see a group of works by Chillida, the great Basque sculptor, and Tàpies, the great Catalan painter, and we added works by these artists to the collection.

Actually this was another element of good luck and good fortune because the exterior surface is titanium, and Frank knew he wanted a metal surface. We experimented endlessly with stainless steel. We distressed stainless steel, we poured acid on it, we drove over it on trucks, we dragged it through stones, we blasted it with sand, we hit it with pebbles, we scratched it, we scuffed it, we tried to make stainless steel work. Somebody suggested titanium and titanium was just impossibly costly, so we thought titanium was out of the question. However, as it happened, in the summer of 1995 the price of titanium started to go down. And by the end of the summer into early fall 1995 the actual bulk price of titanium dipped below that of stainless steel. So we bought titanium futures for future delivery. Right after we made the purchase the price went back up and so indeed somebody was smiling on the project. But the project's

Views, Guggenheim Museum Bilbao, Frank O. Gehry, December 1995

View, Guggenheim Museum Bilbao, Frank O. Gehry, 1995

distinctive feature, I think, is the way it absorbs and reflects the light. I have never seen any-thing like this. It just activates the city in such an incredible way as one of its great features. And the other great feature – and you do not really realize it when you see the photographs unless you have visited it – is its enormous scale. This is a scale drawing of the Guggenheim Museum in New York, the Guggenheim Museum Bilbao, the Metropolitan Museum in New York, and the Sydney Opera House, all on the same scale. Bilbao is on a heroic scale that is where, in many ways, it is indeed like Chartres Cathedral, it just dominates your impression.

You can see how we played with the building and activated it – this was the building before the construction of the Jeff Koons sculpture and the building after the construction of the Jeff Koons sculpture. You had these rather dramatic insights to the building, but I think that its sense of fun and its sense of play, the sense that this kind of interaction between cul-ture and art can be both serious and fascinating and fun at the same time, these were all part of the enjoyment of doing this project. You see it in so many ways. I had never seen a build-ing that looks so different from so many perspectives in every kind of climatic and weather condition. I mean, it is a building that is almost sheer poetry, that is continually reinventing itself, yet it is also based on a very strict rationality of the interior.

What it has done for the Guggenheim – to bring us back to the definition of the museum – is that it has created a larger reality. Right now I see the project about halfway done, and I do not

know exactly where that is going to go next, but there are a lot of opportunities out there, because the success of Bilbao in the number of visitors, and the quality of the programming and the collections, has not escaped attention. And there are interesting opportunities and forces out there for us to continue to develop. However, I also realize that things are getting very, very sophisticated, and that in many ways what I do now is that I manage a brand and that brand is the Guggenheim. I do not know yet where that will take us, I cannot say in advance that it is necessarily bad. We are aware of the pitfalls and what this means. I think it means perhaps a more conservative operational style for the institution in the next few years. Nevertheless I am aware that everything that we do now from a programmatic standpoint or certainly from an architectural standpoint contributes to that perception of the institution as a brand. And here is the reality. We actually think like that sometimes, and I do not believe that it compromises what I would call our intellectual or academic integrity; in fact quite the reverse is true. I think that we are adept in this area — when I say we, I mean the people I work with — I think that we are adept at keeping a firewall between these two opposite poles because we also recognize that those opposite poles are necessary.

It was Hugo Boss that allowed us to spend the 500,000 dollars that we needed to install the *Puppy Dog* in Bilbao as a permanent piece of sculpture. Without that funding we would not have been able to do it, so for a brief moment we dressed up that *Puppy Dog* in a Hugo Boss suit and then pulled it off and that was the end of it. Hugo Boss has used that a couple of times, but

View, Guggenheim Museum Bilbao, Frank O. Gehry

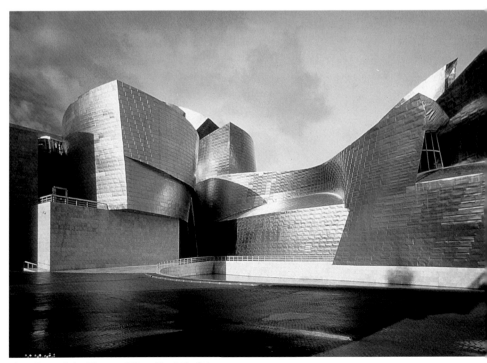

View, Guggenheim Museum Bilbao, Frank O. Gehry

View, Guggenheim Museum Bilbao, Frank O. Gehry

Entrance, Guggenheim Museum Bilbao, Frank O. Gehry, and Jeff Koons, *Puppy Dog*

View, Guggenheim Museum Bilbao, Frank O. Gehry

View, Guggenheim Museum Bilbao, Frank O. Gehry

that project will always be there and it gets planted three times a year, and Jeff is continually reinterpreting the skin of the *Puppy Dog* by the choice of the colors of the flowers. It is absolutely wild, and it is a terrific, terrific piece. But this notion that the Guggenheim is something that we have to protect – that we have to protect our traditional and cultural integrity – is a very powerful message that runs with the institution.

This brings me to my last two images: the Guggenheim had the great good fortune to be defined by two extraordinary architectural moments: the Guggenheim Museum in Bilbao and the Frank Lloyd Wright Building in New York City. One hopes that this is not the end of that. I can maybe see myself playing at this for a couple of more years at least. It is a lot of fun; you get to meet a lot of great people, and every once in a while you get a card like this that says "special guest," you know, it is blue and gold, it comes from the MAK here in Vienna and it symbolizes my close relationship with Peter Noever, my respect for his work, my friendships with Hans Hollein, Agnes Husslein, Wolf Prix, all the other people in Vienna that have been so generous with their time, energy, ideas, and commitment in making the Guggenheim Museum a reality. So it is a very special moment for me to be here. Thank you all for having me, and I hope you found this at least somewhat interesting.

THE CONSTRUCTION OF A PLACE: BUILDING WITH NICHOLAS GRIMSHAW, FRANK O. GEHRY, TADAO ANDO, ZAHA HADID, AND ALVARO SIZA VIEIRA

Rolf Fehlbaum

Rolf Fehlbaum

The place we are talking about is on the outskirts of Weil am Rhein, a small German town of about 28,000 inhabitants. Weil am Rhein is situated right next to Basel and would have become one of its suburbs if it were not for the border that separates the two.

The building site is shaped like a triangle with one side opening towards a vineyard, while another side is formed by a major road and railroad tracks and the third side faces the town that is slowly growing closer to the site.

This triangle constitutes the plot occupied by the Vitra factory complex whose buildings have been designed over the past 18 years by the architects Nicholas Grimshaw, Frank O. Gehry, Tadao Ando, Zaha Hadid and Alvaro Siza Vieira.

The planning of the site was not based on any visionary strategy; instead the planning process has occurred as a step-by-step development resulting from personal encounters with architects and designers and the economic development of the company.

The most decisive influence on the Vitra architecture was my early encounters with Charles and Ray Eames and George Nelson, the American designers whose furniture designs have been produced by Vitra since the late 1950s. They introduced me to modern architecture and opened my eyes to the buildings in my native city of Basel and its surroundings, in particular Dornach with the Goetheanum and Ronchamp.

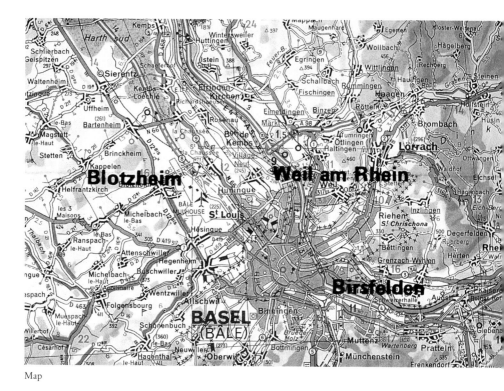

Map

Vitra Factory Area, Weil am Rhein

In the United States, especially in California, I experienced a different kind of modernism, a modernism that was not hard and severe, but combined a sparse structure with a playful interior, as e.g. in Eames House. Santa Monica and nearby Venice, where Charles and Ray Eames lived and worked, later became important for me again through my encounter with Frank Gehry.

Initially it was a matter of working with European designers, and my contacts with Verner Panton in the 1960s and Mario Bellini in the 1970s showed me that there were many other possibilities for solving a particular design problem besides the Eames approach. This was the basis for the pluralist approach that also manifests itself in the architecture of the Vitra company.

In 1981 a major fire destroyed more than half of our factory buildings. This event, which in hindsight turns out to have been an act of creative destruction, presented an opportunity to purposefully choose the architecture of the new buildings. Instead of commissioning some local building contractor to simply rebuild the plant as it had been, we decided to commission Nicholas Grimshaw, whose factory buildings in England I had gone to see shortly before.

The factory building which Grimshaw designed was a simple elongated body, to which other elements containing the lounges, sanitary facilities and staircases were attached.

This new factory building worked so well and was so satisfying aesthetically that I commissioned Grimshaw to also develop a master plan for the entire company site. At the time it seemed to me ideal to have the entire grounds covered with these gleaming factory buildings by Grimshaw.

This idea was challenged, however, when in 1984 we presented my father for his 70th birthday with a sculpture that had been created specifically for this site by Claes Oldenburg and Coosje van Bruggen. The sculpture, entitled *Balancing Tools*, represented a certain irritation, a criticism of the smoothness and uniformity of the place that were beginning to become evident.

This contact with Claes Oldenburg and Coosje van Bruggen also led to our encounter with Frank Gehry, whom I commissioned to design a chair for our company. The result was Gehry's *Little Beaver* design for the Vitra Edition, a chair made of corrugated cardboard whose contours appear to be slowly disintegrating. This piece of furniture led to our discussion about the collection of modern furniture which I was assembling at the time and the space in which this furniture exhibition could be shown.

As the company continued to expand and another factory building became necessary we abandoned the previous master plan and commissioned Frank Gehry to build it. As a kind of additional bonus we decided to treat ourselves to a small museum building to be located directly in front of the production facilities. This building became the Vitra Design Museum, which is today far more than a mere exhibition gallery for our collection. Headed by Alexander von Vegesack, the Vitra Design Museum has become an internationally renowned institution that reaches a large audience through its travelling exhibitions, publications and workshops.

The factory building, the Vitra Design Museum and the porter's lodge are three episodes by Frank Gehry that present themselves in ever new constellations as one walks across the company grounds. Gehry invested just as much creative energy in the design of the simple factory building as in the museum, and as always in his work this interplay of expressiveness and simplicity heightens the charm of the expressive. Incidentally, the factory building with its large windows and distant views is very popular with our employees.

I am convinced that the new architecture on the Vitra grounds has charged our company with new energy and strengthened its cohesiveness: the message that is conveyed by these buildings every day increases the identification of the employees with the company.

The juxtaposition of Nicholas Grimshaw's and Frank Gehry's factory buildings, both of which have identical dimensions, was a test of our new approach. Frank Gehry took up Grimshaw's basic idea, responding to Grimshaw's towers with his own towers. In my opinion the formal differences and contrasting architectural approaches represent a positive and enriching confrontation. This encouraged us to continue to think and plan along the same lines of heterogeneity.

I became convinced that one architect alone could never give the place the kind of vitality and urbanism that is the result of such confrontations. However, one decisive aspect was the willingness of every "new" architect to address the existing buildings and the fact that despite their different ways of expression the architects should share some fundamental val-

Vitra Factory Building, Nicholas Grimshaw

Vitra Design Museum, Frank O. Gehry

Vitra Factory Building, Nicholas Grimshaw

Vitra Design Museum, Frank O. Gehry, and sculpture *Balancing Tools* by Claes Oldenburg and Coosje van Bruggen, 1984

Interior, Vitra Design Museum, Frank O. Gehry

ues. This has been the basis for our choice of architects. In this way a concept has been chosen that rather than being based on a trivial harmony tolerates and even encourages contradiction and conflict as long as they do not turn into enmity.

Our next project was the conference building by Tadao Ando, whom I had met at a lecture in Basel that had been organized by Werner Blaser. My original idea had been to have him do a kind of meditation room that I called the "Pavilion of Silence." In the course of time it turned into something else, namely the conference center. Tadao Ando followed along graciously with this change in project from the Pavilion of Silence to conference center. The major challenge in this case was the direct neighborhood of Gehry's expressive museum building.

The different approaches of the two architects manifested themselves not only in the shapes of their respective buildings. Gehry had turned the building site, a cherry orchard into a *tabula rasa*, leaving only a single row of trees. Ando, on the other hand, planned his building in the midst of the cherry orchard in such a way that in the end no more than three trees had to be cut down. This approach to nature makes the building almost disappear in its setting. Everything is planned with the scale of the trees in mind; the building was to be low enough so that the trees would still dominate. In accordance with this idea the building was lowered by one story.

Ando's building maintained the idea of the Pavilion of Silence by facing away from the factory and being accessible only via a zigzag path that eventually runs along a wall. By the time you have arrived there you are, as it were, purified, even though it has really taken you just a few steps.

Although the layout of the path and the wall manifests a certain turning away from the museum building, this gesture is intentional and expresses the underlying idea. Gehry's museum is a museum of everyday life and should therefore be easily accessible. The Conference Center, on the other hand, should only be reached by specific people and not too many of them. The path leading there, the reduced height of the building with its courtyard and spartan furnishings, all convey seclusion. And that corresponds to the program.

The next building to be realized was the fire station planned with Zaha Hadid. It was Zaha Hadid's first building. It provided us with an opportunity to analyze the site with her. None of the other architects concerned themselves so intensely with the site and its relationship to the surrounding landscape. In hundreds of drawings and studies design ideas for the fire station were related to the lines of the landscape, the roads and railroad tracks, the field formations and existing buildings. The fire station was to serve not only the fire brigade, but also to impart a recognizable shape to the site. The building is located at the end of the main axis crossing the company grounds, where the Vitra site meets the city of Weil, which unfortunately does not present itself too well here from an architectural point of view. Zaha did not simply situate her long building parallel to the main axis, but shifted the latter towards the end and juxtaposed the parts of her building in such a way that they emphasize the edge of the company site. At the same time the building serves a protective function against the outside world, thus helping to define the place.

Much has been said about the extraordinary spatial quality of this building. However, the building really has to be experienced, since photographs can capture it only in parts and only its most expressive aspects. The contextual significance of the building for the site and the spatial experience involved cannot be conveyed by photography.

Today Zaha Hadid's building is no longer used as a fire station, since this task has been taken over by the city of Weil under more favorable conditions. Instead Hadid's building has been turned into an annex to the museum, a function which it fulfils no less successfully than it did its original function as a fire station.

In keeping with a long-standing wish of mine, I eventually managed to get into contact with Alvaro Siza through Frank Gehry's intervention. It had become necessary to build another factory, and this had to be in close proximity to Hadid's building, Gehry's building and Grimshaw's factory – in other words, in an already very complex location. With reference to this neighborhood Siza decided on a very simple, unobtrusive building. His building made of engineering brick gives the impression of an anonymous factory. He was particularly fascinated by the long, uniform outside walls and it was only after intensive discussions that he put in several windows – rather than a single one in the middle.

Another task of Siza's was to create a link between Grimshaw's factory building and his own that would be able to protect the movement of goods and people from rain and snow. From the very beginning Siza wanted to erect a high bridge connecting the buildings – but how was that supposed to provide protection from rain and snow? A low bridge was out of the question for him, since it would have blocked the view of Zaha Hadid's building. In the end he had the idea of constructing the high bridge in such a way that it is lowered by means of sensors whenever it is raining or snowing, thus offering protection while otherwise allowing an unobstructed, framed view of the fire station. Despite initial doubts we may say today that over time this bridge has assumed an important role for the entire site by providing cohesion between the individual buildings. What had previously been an assemblage of disparate buildings has been turned into a whole by means of this bridge, which soars above

Vitra Conference Center, Tadao Ando

Vitra Conference Center, Tadao Ando

Grimshaw's factory. It has probably become the single most important integrational element of the entire site.

The place continues to develop. What had originally been intended as an industrial production facility with uniform buildings has become something quite different. The uniformity which one normally expects of an industrial plant – and as a rule industry strives to express this clarity and uniformity – has been abandoned in favor of uncertainty and a willingness to tolerate conflict. What is important about these buildings is no longer clarity, symmetry and a certain hierarchy; instead they are episodes that can be read in different ways. Complexity and contradiction have become the expression of a new corporate culture.

The fact that an enterprise is no longer monolithic and characterized by uniformity, but instead presents a way of thinking that involves change and renewal and dealing with uncertainties, seems to me an appropriate contemporary concept of corporate identity.

Another important aspect for us has been the idea not to separate the cultural activity from the production activities. Basically the museum could have been equally erected in Paris, Vienna, or anywhere else – in that case many more people would come to visit it – but the interesting fact about it is precisely that it is located on a factory site, that, if you want to put it this way, the idealized superstructure to our everyday life has been created here. Of course it had never been our idea to exhibit the company's own products in a museum. What has always been of importance to us is the history and the presentation of design and lately increasingly also architecture.

At the Vitra site the borderline between the cultural and the commercial activities becomes blurred. Leisure and work, the public and the non-public happen in the same place. In this way a richer and more complex industrial landscape is created – a place rather than a mere factory complex.

Building with architects who would never have built here if it had not been for Vitra and with elements not indigenous to this region has been important in order to define this specific place and build an identity of our own. This also explains why I have so far not commissioned any architects from Basel, even though some of them are great. If one lives in the province one has to create a link to the world and an ambiguity by differentiating it from the familiar. For me it has always been clear that architecture should not express the identity of the company but that the latter is instead created by the way the site is being built up and constructed. For this reason it has been so important for this place to concern ourselves with the unfamiliar from outside and it is only at this point imaginable and indeed desirable to enrich the place with a building designed by an architect from Basel.

A FEW WORDS ON PRACTICAL MATTERS

When working with foreign architects a certain division of labor is necessary. The chosen architect analyzes the basic requirements, does the preliminary planning, designs the building and plans part of its construction. On the other hand getting the design approved, planning the remaining part of the construction and supervising the building activity are done by the local contact architect. This has always worked out well, even before the existence of e-mail, when everything had to be clarified by faxes sent between the offices.

Vitra Fire Station, Zaha Hadid

Vitra Fire Station, Zaha Hadid

Vitra Fire Station, Zaha Hadid

Vitrashop Factory, Alvaro Siza Vieira

The frequently asked question whether building with such architects – sometimes they are also referred to as star architects – has been more expensive, has to be answered with a qualified "yes." In the case of small buildings planned with a lot of effort and investment of time the cost of planning and construction was definitely higher than average. However, in the case of the large factory buildings the difference was negligible. In relation to the entire company site the additional cost is insignificant.

The excessive construction faults and weaknesses occasionally predicted by visiting civil engineers have not occurred so far, and in view of the high quality of the buildings we gladly accept responsibility for a certain amount of maintenance.

The next new building was erected not in Weil but on the nearby Swiss company site in Birsfelden. This is where Vitra's very first factory building was erected in the 1950s and is still in use today. On the vacant part of the lot the Vitra headquarters was to be built, a very informal office building that needed to respond to the complex ambience of this site, correspond to our attitude and yet be suitable to be partly rented out, since we did not want to use the entire building ourselves. It was clear to me that meeting these demands was going to be difficult, and I wanted to tackle this task once again with Frank Gehry.

The situation in Birsfelden is very different from that in Weil. In Weil we were building on open terrain, whereas in Birsfelden we enter into a web of relationships that have devel-

Vitrashop Factory, Alvaro Siza Vieira

Vitrashop Factory, Alvaro Siza Vieira

oped between the adjacent residential area, commercial buildings, allotment gardens and an autobahn ramp. The building to be erected there was to be individualistic and yet not disturb the existing interplay between these factors. Frank Gehry's concept was to organize the building mass in such a way that it appears to be small-scale, revealing its individuality only from close up. A regular office block that hardly distinguishes itself from its surroundings in terms of its height and materials, is placed perpendicular to the road. Connected to it by an atrium but set back from the road is the villa, the central part of the building, with its expressive conference rooms, cafeteria and entrance. The three elements are connected by a common wing-like roof that binds them together.

The building is so well-integrated into its surroundings that it has been awarded the prize of the "Heimatschutz" organization which is as a rule dedicated to preserving the status quo. Gehry also cooperated on the interior design and designed the lights for the various rooms.

After 1994 there was a break in our building activity since we had now sufficient space available. Our concern with architecture took a different turn then. We acquired the Barragán Archive and have been organizing and cataloguing it in preparation for an exhibition and publication, and we have begun to organize architectural exhibitions at the Vitra Design Museum.

Recently, however, we have been discussing plans for building again. A factory project for a site 30 kilometers north of Weil has been developed together with MVRDV. Its realization, however, is not yet certain, since new considerations concerning the site have emerged.

One thing that is certain, though, is that we want to commission Frank Gehry to expand the museum. The challenge here is to add a new element to Gehry's carefully balanced existing elements of museum, factory and porter's lodge. A solution seems to be in sight, but the final design is still being developed.

Other projects are the possibility of building in the immediate vicinity of the fire station with Zaha Hadid, and developing a landscaping concept for the site with Adriaan Geuze from Rotterdam.

This brings me almost to the end of our tour of the company grounds. It is only now that I realize the link between this place and Los Angeles. The people who have influenced it the most were neighbors: Charles and Ray Eames and Frank Gehry all lived in Santa Monica and worked in nearby Venice. Gehry's former office was only a few hundred yards away from 901 Washington Boulevard, where the Eameses had their office. And I realize today that it was this journey from Basel and Weil to Los Angeles and back which has determined the place and that which has since happened there.

Vitra Center Birsfelden, Frank O. Gehry

Why spend so much time thinking about the architecture and construction of a place? A variety of tentative explanations are offered from outside: being a patron of the arts on the one hand, a clever business idea on the other. Both are missing the point. Working with the architects and designers, jointly building up the place and the enterprise, is an eminently satisfying and useful process, stimulating for everyone involved, a learning process. This is sufficient reason.

That this energy also has a positive effect on the development of the company is an obvious side effect.

WHAT ABOUT THE FUTURE?

I hope that we will continue to build and that globalization and virtualization will not result in cutting us off from the site. This is where I see the greatest danger for the architecture of enterprises. If companies determine their site by the cost of labor and tax breaks or are forced to do so they will become nomads that are no longer interested in the stability and permanence of a site. I hope that we will find the right conditions on our company site that will permit us to continue working towards the further development of the place for a long time to come.

Vitra Center Birsfelden, Frank O. Gehry

Interior view, Vitra Center Birsfelden, Frank O. Gehry

"YOU DA MAN!"

Philip Johnson

If a potential client comes to you and offers you the opportunity to do the cheapest skyscraper, you don't accept that. Well, I don't. Because you can't make architecture unless the program is reasonable. This is why I described the redo of the Museum of Modern Art as "an impossible job for an impossible site." Its program is an obstacle to the making of great architecture. You also want a client (or *patron*) who works with you, who is *sympathisch*. It's OK if the client says *no* to some things, as long as the client participates. You want a partner like Alfred Barr, who as the Museum of Modern Art's first director worked with me on the design of the MoMA garden. Of course, the classic example was my relationship with Mrs. Bliss when we did the museum that she commissioned at Dumbarton Oaks in Washington, DC. She and I worked with full-size mock-ups of the structure as part of the design process. Now I find myself talking shop with the pastor of my upcoming Cathedral of Hope in Texas. I have always preferred commissions where I work with the client.

Take the papacy – there you can find partnerships that produced truly magnificent architecture. Those papal patrons of Michelangelo, Borromini and Bernini didn't care how much those projects cost – they wanted glory – and they got it! Money, however, isn't the real issue. Reasonable cost can lead to perfectly good architecture – as long as the rapport with the client works.

When you are your own client, as I have been at the Glass House, it's harder because you criticize yourself more. But that situation is very rare and not fair as a comparison. It's such a private masturbation. When I recently reexamined my design for the new chapel at the Glass House, I realized I just didn't like it. I changed it *again*. There is a real advantage to having a patron/partner.

How did Michelangelo do it with Julius II? Or Haussmann with Napoleon III? I don't know. What I do know is that Edgar Kaufmann was right there on the site when Frank Lloyd Wright was creating Fallingwater. He devoted his energies, just as Wright did, to the success of that wonderful house. The same occurred with Hib Johnson, the patron of Wright's Johnson Wax headquarters. Wright couldn't have done it without such clients. When you have a great patron and program, then you can get architecture.

Edited by Hilary Lewis

APPENDIX

Rolf Fehlbaum

Born in Basel in 1941, Rolf Fehlbaum studied social sciences in Freiburg im Breisgau, Munich, Berne and Basel, graduating from Basel University in 1967 with a dissertation about Utopian Socialism (academic adviser: Edgar Salin). The dissertation was awarded the "Genossenschaftspreis der Stadt Basel." A revised version entitled *Saint-Simon und die Saint-Simonisten – vom Laissez-Faire zur Wirtschaftsplanung* was published by J.C.B. Mohr in 1970. Fehlbaum and two partners then founded the Multiple-Verlag X-art Collection. Later Fehlbaum worked as a producer of documentary films for Bavaria München and from 1973 on he was "Referent für Aus- und Fortbildung" for the Bavarian Chamber of Architects in Munich.

In 1977 Fehlbaum became director of Vitra and turned the company into one of the leading European furniture manufacturers with design lines by Charles and Ray Eames and George Nelson, Verner Panton, Mario Bellini, Antonio Citterio, Jasper Morrison and Philippe Starck. From 1983 on he began to assemble a comprehensive collection of modern furniture. Rolf Fehlbaum initiated the Vitra Design Museum, which opened in November 1989, and he commissioned well-known international architects such as Frank O. Gehry, Nicholas Grimshaw, Tadao Ando, Alvaro Siza Vieira and Zaha M. Hadid to design buildings for Vitra. It should be pointed out that the Vitra Design Museum together with a factory building were Frank Gehry's first European project, Tadao Ando's Conference Center was Ando's first commission outside of Japan, Zaha Hadid's fire station that architect's first built project and Alvaro Siza's factory his first industrial building and project in this part of the world.

In 1991 Rolf Fehlbaum was awarded the Prize of Industrie Forum Design Hannover (iF) for his extraordinary achievements in the field of promoting design and public commissions of design projects. In conjunction with the award the book by Rolf Fehlbaum, *Vitra, Vom Umgang mit Design, Gegenwart und Ökonomie* (Steidl 1991) was published. In 1994 Fehlbaum was awarded the Lucky Strike Design Award of the Raymond Loewy Foundation and in 1997 the German Federal Award for Design Promotion.

Dates and Facts about Vitra

Vitra is an international furniture company. It produces and markets furniture for offices, public areas and home interiors. Vitra's clients include leading international companies and institutions. Its products are the result of cooperation with major designers. The Vitra Design Museum – independent of the company – houses a collection of over 2000 exhibits on design. It conceives and holds exhibitions that are later shown at museums around the world, as well as arranging workshops for designers, people interested in design, and children. Moreover, it publishes exhibition catalogues and markets a collection of miniatures of classical furniture designs.

Chairman: Rolf Fehlbaum
Headquarters: Basel–Birsfelden (Switzerland), Weil am Rhein (Germany)
Manufacturing: Weil am Rhein (Germany)
Plants: Neuenburg (Germany)
                     Allentown, PA (U.S.A.)
Sales: Switzerland, Germany, Austria, Belgium, Spain
Organisations and
Showrooms: France, Great Britain, Netherlands, U.S.A., Saudi Arabia
Representations: Australia, Hongkong, Japan, Singapore, Scandinavia and others
Turnover 1997:   DM 338 million
Staff: Approx. 620

Awards:
1991   Design Prize Switzerland
1994   Corporate Design Award, iF Industrie Forum Design Hannover
1994   European Community Design Award

History

1934   Takeover of shop-fitting business by Willi Fehlbaum, founder of the Vitra enterprise in Basel, Switzerland

1950   Set-up of Vitra Germany in Weil am Rhein

1957/58   Licenced production of the *Herman Miller Collection* (designs by Charles & Ray Eames and George Nelson)

1966/67   Introduction of the *Panton Chair* by Verner Panton

1976   Introduction of *Vitramat*: a new solution for an ergonomic office chair range

1979   Start of co-operation with Mario Bellini

1984   Introduction of the *Bellini Collection*: Office chairs: *Persona, Figura, Imago* (design: Mario Bellini with Dieter Thiel)

1986   Vitra takes over all rights on Eames and Nelson models for Europe and the Middle East.

The dichotomy of West and East is constantly evoked in Ando's oeuvre, most palpably in the chapel in the Rokko Mountains in Kobe (1985–86), where glazed-in Shinto-style arcades lead to a hollow in the mountainside while also serving as access to a Western basilica next to it. Only on rare occasions has Ando foregone the use of concrete: in two tea-houses and especially in his great wooden pavilion for EXPO 1992 in Seville. In 1993 he designed the Conference Center for the Vitra company in Weil am Rhein, the architect's first building outside of Japan. His latest works are museum buildings, such as the Museum of Wood in Hyogo (1994) and the Oyamazaki Villa Museum in Kyoto (1996).
Selected awards:
1989 Gold Medal of Architecture, French Academy of Architecture
1995 Pritzker Prize
1997 Royal Gold Medal, Royal Institute of British Architects

Frank O. Gehry

Frank O. Gehry was born in Toronto in 1929 and studied at the University of Southern California in Los Angeles and at Harvard University in Cambridge, Massachusetts. After 1953 he worked for Victor Gruen, Hideo Sasaki and William Pereira among others, before establishing his own practice in Los Angeles in 1962.

Gehry's architectural oeuvre, which started locally in Southern California but has by now certainly achieved global dimensions, cannot be categorized either theoretically or stylistically. After designing interiors and store fittings Gehry built a number of single-family houses in the early 1970s which were characterized by an increasing dissolution of tectonic conventions as e.g. in Gehry's own house in Santa Monica (1977–79, 1988). This house – which was basically a remodelling of an existing building – breaks down existing tectonic structures and spatial boundaries in order to restructure them antithetically, overlayed by additional reclaimed materials, thus representing a program building of Deconstructivism. Gehry's friendship with the sculptors Richard Serra and Claes Oldenburg influenced a number of increasingly sculptural buildings in the 1980s that led to a veritable boom in commissions for Gehry. The result was a series of figural compositions and sculptural decompositions such as the California Aerospace Museum in Los Angeles (1982–84).

Gehry's architectural projects from the '90s, including the American Center in Paris (1988–93), the Vitra administrative and office building in Birsfelden near Basel (1990–94), the Energy Forum Innovation Building in Bad Oeynhausen (1992–95), the Nationale-Nederlanden Building in Prague (1992–97) and the Goldstein subsidized housing project in Frankfurt am Main (1996) are increasingly sculptural, irrational shapes designed with the aid of computers, whereby objective functional concerns are clearly overlaid by the subjective appearance of spaces, shapes and colors. A key role in this context is played by Gehry's numerous museum buildings, such as the Vitra Design Museum in Weil am Rhein (1987–89), the Frederick R. Weisman Art Museum in Minneapolis, Minnesota (1990–93) and the Guggenheim Museum in Bilbao, Spain (1991–97).

Selected awards:

1977 Arnold W. Brunner Memorial Prize, American Academy of Arts and Letters

1989 Pritzker Prize

1992 Wolf Prize in Art, Wolf Foundation

1998 Austrian Friedrich Kiesler-Prize for Architecture and the Arts

1999 AIA Gold Medal, American Institute of Architects

Nicholas Grimshaw

Born in Hove, Great Britain, in 1939, Grimshaw first studied architecture at Edinburgh College of Art, finishing his studies at the Architectural Association in London. In 1965, together with Terry Farrell, he founded the Farrell Grimshaw partnership, which existed until 1980. Their architectural office became well known for their work with prefabricated and standardized building components as e.g. in the Citroen branch office in Runnymede (1972). After dissolving the partnership Grimshaw continued to work in industral architecture as a believer in the idea of a purely functional architecture. He built a gymnasium for IBM in Winchester (1980), a factory building for the furniture manufacturer Vitra in Weil am Rhein (1981) and a distribution center for Herman Miller in Chippenham (1982). The common feature of these buildings is an independent outside skin covering a supporting structure of steel or concrete. Another important theme of his has been revealing the actual construction, especially in the case of towers or masts from which the roof is suspended with wire cables.

In 1993 Grimshaw completed his most important building in London: the international terminal for Eurostar trains at Waterloo Station, where a glass unit is built in such a way that it follows the curved tracks. That same year he finished the new terminal at London's Heathrow Airport, with its shapes like compressed tubes reminiscent of aircraft fuselages, while the main hall extends under a huge curved surface that resembles the wing of an airplane. These projects reveal the architect's intention to create a metaphorical skin for the rational industrial production process.

Current work includes the masterplanning and redevelopment of Paddington Station, London, the redevelopment of Zurich Airport, a new main line railway station and urban design in Pusan, Korea, an art gallery in La Coruña, Spain, and a touring industrial design exhibition called FUSION. Grimshaw is also engaged in the design of four Millennium Commission funded projects: the Eden Project in Cornwall, the National Space Science Centre in Leicester, Millennium Point at Digbeth near Birmingham and Bath Spa.

Selected awards:

1993 CBE

1994 Building of the Year Award from the Royal Institute of British Architects

1994 Mies van der Rohe Pavilion Award for European Architecture

Zaha M. Hadid

Zaha Hadid, who was born in Baghdad, Iraq, in 1950, first completed her studies of Mathematics at the American University of Baghdad before studying architecture at London's Architectural Association. She was strongly influenced by her teachers Elia Zenghelis and Rem Koolhaas. In 1977 she joined the newly founded OMA (Office for Metropolitan Architecture) and participated in their competition entry for the extension to the building of the Dutch Parliament. Soon afterwards she established her own practice with competition entries for the residence of the Irish Prime Minister (1980), the Parc de la Villette in Paris (1982) and the Hong Kong Peak complex (1983). In addition to her dynamic architectural potential, the spectacularly colorful drawings and paintings of her early works attracted much attention. Her first built design was the fire station made of reinforced concrete for the Vitra company in Weil am Rhein (1989–93). In the same year she completed a subsidized housing project at the International Building Exhibition (IBA) in Berlin. In 1994 she won the international competition for the opera house in Cardiff but local politics prevented its realization. Central to her concerns is a simultaneous engagement in practice, teaching and research, in a pursuit of an uncompromising commitment to modernism. Her work encompasses all fields of design, ranging from the urban scale to products, interiors and furniture. She also created the installation design for the exhibition *Wish Machine – World Invention* for Kunsthalle Vienna. Ongoing schemes include a housing project in Vienna, an exhibition pavilion at the Landesgartenschau in Weil am Rhein and The New Millennium Experience Dome, Mind Zone in London.

Recently Zaha Hadid has been named the winner of a worldwide competition for a contemporary art center in Rome and construction is soon to begin on her Contemporary Art Center in Cincinnati. Zaha Hadid lives and works in London.

Selected awards:

1982 Gold Medal in Architectural Design, British Architecture, for 59 Eaton Place, London

1995 Special Award, Royal Academy Summer Exhibition

Eric Owen Moss

Born in 1943, Eric Owen Moss studied architecture at the University of California, Berkeley, and at Harvard University. Since 1974 he has been Professor of Design and a member of the Trustees of the Southern California Institute of Architecture. In 1976 he established his own practice in Culver City, Los Angeles County.

Eric Owen Moss is one of the most important representatives of a new Californian architecture. One recurring theme in his work is the dialogue with pre-existing structures, evident in the conversion of an abandoned factory plant in Culver City (1986–90) and the former industrial building Lindblade Tower (1987–89). The use of elements of industrial mass production and structural dissonances point to the development of a new aesthetic. Current projects include buildings in Vienna, Spain, France, New York, Los Angeles and Culver City.

His latest completed buildings are the 100-meter-long Samitaur office block, headquarters for Eastman Kodak, and the PS Building, headquarters of an international digital design firm. Upcoming projects include high-rise towers in Los Angeles, the Stealth building in Culver City, and residential projects in Hollywood and Calabassas. Moss is the recipient of 35 design awards from Progressive Architecture and the American Institute of Architecture and is a fellow of the American Institute of Architecture.

Alvaro Joaquim de Melo Siza Vieira

Born in Matosinhos, Portugal, in 1933. After studying architecture at the Escola Superior de Belas Artes in Oporto and working for his former teacher, the influential architect Fernando Távora, Siza established his own architectural practice in 1958. Siza's early projects are characterized by a striving to connect his architecture to the surrounding landscape, combined with elements from the formal language of classical modernism. Gradually these developed into the identifiable attributes of Siza's critical aesthetic approach.

Despite the usual number of projects that could not be built, in recent years Siza has succeeded in expanding the scope of his practical activity, which ranges from the Malaguiera Quarter project in Évora (since 1977) to the School of Architecture on the banks of the Douro in Oporto, built between 1986–95. In addition to subsidized housing developments in the Hague and Berlin and the rebuilding of the Chiado Quarter in Lisbon (1988–97) that had been destroyed by fire, three important buildings confirm Siza's high rank as a socially committed architect: the Teacher Training College in Setúbal (1988–94), the Galician Center for Contemporary Art in Santiago de Compostela (1988–94) and the University Library in Aveiro (1988–95). The factory building for the Vitra company in Weil am Rhein built in 1991 was Siza's first industrial building. His latest important works are the Portuguese Pavilion for EXPO 1998 in Lisbon and the Museum Serralves in Oporto (1999).
Selected awards:
1992 Pritzker Prize
1993 National Architecture Prize of the Portuguese Architects' Association
1998 Arnold W. Brunner Memorial Prize of the American Academy of Arts and Letters,
   New York

Philip Cortelyou Johnson

Born in 1906 in Cleveland, Ohio, where he was schooled in German philosophy and literature, Johnson entered Harvard University in 1923, graduating in 1930 with degrees in philosophy and classics. While at Harvard, Johnson made the acquaintance of Alfred Barr, a professor at Wellesley College and soon to be the first director of the Museum of Modern Art, and befriended Henry-Russel Hitchcock, the great American architectural historian, then a Harvard graduate student. These contacts led to Johnson's tour of modern European architecture with Hitchcock which in 1932 resulted in their co-authored landmark book and show at the Museum of Modern Art *The International Style: Architecture since 1922.*

From 1932 to 1934 Johnson served as the first Director of Architecture and Design at the Museum of Modern Art. From 1934 to 1940 Johnson left architecture for political activities in the U.S. and Germany. The time spent in Germany, in addition to an earlier stay there in the 1920s, brought Johnson into contact with the leading figures of the Bauhaus, including Walter Gropius and Mies van der Rohe. Johnson then returned to Harvard where he received his B.Arch. in 1943.

Johnson's attitude towards architecture can be summarized as a desire for elegance of materials and line, combined with an ironic approach to forms often, but not always historic. While still at Harvard, Johnson built his first building, a house for himself in Cambridge, Massachusetts (1942), based on Mies van der Rohe's idea for a courthouse and a precursor to Johnson's Glass House in New Canaan, Connecticut (1949). The building used prefabricated materials, then the rage in architectural teaching, and served as Johnson's graduate thesis.

By the 1950s Johnson began to receive some institutional commissions, which included the Kneses Tifereth Israel Synagogue in Port Chester, New York (1956) and the Abby Aldrich Rockefeller Sculpture Garden of the Museum of Modern Art (1953). In the 1960s museums became a Johnson speciality. He designed e.g. the Munson-Williams-Proctor Institute in Utica, New York (1960), the Art Gallery in Bielefeld, Germany (1968), and the Museum of Television and Radio in New York City (1991). In the late 1960s Johnson formed a long-term partnership with John Burgee that would result in one of Johnson's busiest and most prolific periods: PPG Corporate Headquarters (1979–84), Transco Tower and Park (1979–85) and Johnson's most famous silhouette, that of the AT&T Corporate Headquarters (1979–84), which became an emblem for the postmodernist movement. Much of Johnson's recent work has been in large commercial projects, such as Riverside South Housing (1996-97) and the Trump International Tower (1995–97). Today, Philip Johnson and his firm Philip Johnson/Alan Ritchie Architects are pursuing pure sculpture as well as incorporating sculptural elements into their architecture. Johnson's Wiener Trio was exhibited at Vienna's MAK – Museum of Applied Arts in 1996 and has been permanently installed in a public space in Vienna since September 1998. His current works include the Cathedral of Hope in Texas, a building for Mass MoCA (Guggenheim), and several commercial projects in the early stages of design development.
Selected awards:
1978 Gold Medal of the American Institute of Architects
1979 Pritzker Price

Joseph Rykwert

Joseph Rykwert is Paul Philippe Cret Professor of Architecture at the University of Pennsylvania and Chairman of their PhD program. He was born in Warsaw and emigrated to England in 1939. Following his architectural studies at the Bartlett School of Architecture and the Architectural Association in London, he taught at Hammersmith School of Arts & Crafts and the Hochschule für Gestaltung, Ulm, before becoming Librarian and Tutor at the Royal College of Art in London. In 1967 he became Professor of Art at the newly-created University of Essex where he remained until 1981 when he became the first Slade Professor in the Fine Arts at the University of Cambridge and then Reader in Architecture. He took up his appointment in Philadelphia in 1988.

Joseph Rykwert has lectured and taught at most major schools of architecture throughout the world and has held visiting appointments in Princeton, the Cooper Union, New York, Harvard Graduate School of Design, the University of Sydney, Louvain, the Institut d'Urbanisme, Paris, the Central European University and others. He has held fellowships at the Center for Advanced Studies in the Visual Arts, Washington, and the Getty Center for the History of Art and the Humanities. His publications include *The Golden House* (1947); *The Idea of a Town* (1963 and two subsequent editions); *On Adam's House in Paradise* (1972 and subsequent editions); *The First Moderns* (1980), *The Necessity of Artifice* (1982, translated into German in 1983); *The Brothers Adam* (1984) (translated into German in 1987), a new translation of Alberti's architecture treatise, *On the Art of Building in Ten Books* (1989, with Robert Tavernor and Neil Leach), and most recently *The Dancing Column* (1996). All his books have been translated into several languages. In 1984, he was appointed Chevalier de l'ordre des Arts et des Lettres. He also holds various honorary degrees and is a member of the Italian Accademia di San Luca.

Selected bibliography

Culver City

Eric Owen Moss, *Buildings and Projects*, New York 1991

Eric Owen Moss, *Buildings and Projects 2*, New York 1996

Eric Owen Moss, *The Box*, New York 1995

Olivier Boissiere, *Eric Owen Moss Architecte, Lindblade Tower & Paramount Laundry: Reconversion à Culver City Californie*, USA, Paris 1990

Architectural Monographs No 29, London 1993: *Eric Owen Moss*

a+u 290, Tokyo 1994 (special issue): *Eric Owen Moss 1974–1994*

GA Document 49, Tokyo 1996: *Eric Owen Moss*

Guggenheim Museum Bilbao

Coosje van Bruggen, *Frank O. Gehry. Guggenheim Museum Bilbao*, Stuttgart 1998

Frank O. Gehry, *Museo Guggenheim Bilbao*, Berlin 1998

GA Document 54, Tokyo 1998: *Guggenheim Bilbao Museum*

Vitra

Stadt und Industriekultur – Industrie und Stadtkultur, Internationaler Workshop Vitra / Weil am Rhein, Basel 1992

Tadao Ando:

Tadao Ando, *Complete Works*, London 1994

Tadao Ando, *The Colours of Light*, London 1996

Tadao Ando, Cologne 1997

Frank O. Gehry:

Frank O. Gehry, *Europäische Projekte*, Berlin 1994

Frank O. Gehry, *Vitra Design Museum*, Stuttgart 1990

Giorgio Romoli, *Frank O. Gehry, Museo Guggenheim, Bilbao*, Torino 1999

GA Document 27, Tokyo 1990, *Frank O. Gehry*

GA Document 40, Tokyo 1994, *Frank O. Gehry*

Nicholas Grimshaw:

Architecture, Industry and Innovation – The Early Work of Nicholas Grimshaw & Partners, London 1995

Architectural Review, July 1983: *Furniture Factory, Weil am Rhein, West Germany*

Capital, May 1990: *Möbelhersteller Vitra*

Deutsche Bauzeitung, December 1983: Gunter Schnel, *Schnelle Kiste*

Diseño Interior, 1994: *Vitra*

Domus 641, Milan 1983: *Ingredienti dell Nouvelle Usine*

L'Architecture d'aujourd'hui, September 1983: *Usine et Bureaux Vitra*

Space Design 244, 1985: *Nicholas Grimshaw & Partners*

World Architecture 41, November 1995: *Grimshaw, Mammon and the MCC*

Zaha Hadid:

Zaha Hadid, *Das Gesamtwerk*, Stuttgart 1998

Zaha Hadid, *Planetary Architecture*, New York 1981

Zaha Hadid, *Planetary Architecture Two*, New York 1983

Elisabeth Blum, *Ein Haus, ein Aufruhr. Anmerkungen zu Zaha Hadids Feuerwehrhaus*, Braunschweig–Wiesbaden 1997

El Croquis 52, Madrid 1991 : Zaha Hadid 1983–1991

Michael Mönninger, *Zaha Hadid, Projekte 1990–1997*, Stuttgart 1998

Alvaro Siza:

Alvaro Siza, *Works & Projects 1954–1992*, Barcelona 1993

Alvaro Siza 1986–1995, Barcelona 1995

a+u, Tokyo 1989 (special issue) Toshio Nakamura (ed.), *Alvaro Siza, 1954–1988*

El Croquis 68/69, Madrid 1994: *Alvaro Siza*

GA Document 49, Tokyo 1996: *Alvaro Siza*

General literature

Burkhard Biella, *Eine Spur ins Wohnen legen. Entwurf einer Philosophie des Wohnens mit Heidegger und über Heidegger hinaus*, Düsseldorf – Bonn 1998

Peter Slake, "Philip Johnson Biography." In: Peter Noever (ed.), *Philip Johnson. Turning Point*, Vienna – New York 1996

Marcel Brion, *Die Medici. Eine Florentiner Familie*, Munich 1979

Jacob Burckhardt, *Die Kultur der Renaissance*, Dresden 1860

Brian Carter, *Johnson Wax Administration Building and Research Tower. Frank Lloyd Wright, Architecture in Detail*, London 1998

Alice T. Friedman, *Women and the Making of the Modern House. A Social and Architectural History*, New York 1998

Frank O. Gehry, "Vorwort." In: Peter Noever (ed.), *Architektur am Ende*, Munich 1993

Daniela Hammer-Tugendhat, Wolf Tegethoff (ed.), *Ludwig Mies van der Rohe. Das Haus Tugendhat*, Vienna – New York 1998

Martin Heidegger, "Bauen, Wohnen, Denken." In: *Vorträge und Aufsätze*, Pfullingen 1978

Ludwig Heydenreich, *Architecture in Italy 1400–1500*, Yale 1996

Thomas S. Hines, *Richard Neutra and the Search for Modern Architecture*, Berkeley – Los Angeles 1994

Rem Koolhaas, *Delirious New York*, New York 1994

Le Corbusier, *Feststellungen* (= Bauwelt Fundamente 12), Braunschweig – Wiesbaden 1987

O.M.A., Rem Koolhaas, Bruce Mau, *S,M,L,XL*, New York 1995

Manfred Sack, "Von der Utopie, dem guten Geschmack und der Kultur des Bauherrn oder: Wie entsteht gute Architektur?" In: Ingeborg Flagge (ed.), *Streiten für die menschliche Stadt*, Hamburg 1997

David Spaeth, *Mies van der Rohe. Der Architekt der technischen Perfektion*, Stuttgart 1995

Gerfried Sperl, *Gegen den Strich gebaut. Essays zur Architektur*, Vienna 1997

Alexej Tarchanow, Sergej Kawtaradse, *Stalinistische Architektur*, Munich 1992